A TREASURY OF
JEWISH FOLKSONG

A TREASURY
OF JEWISH
FOLKSONG

SELECTED AND EDITED BY **Ruth Rubin**

PIANO SETTINGS: Ruth Post · DRAWINGS: T. Herzl Rome

SCHOCKEN BOOKS/NEW YORK

POETRY ADAPTATIONS: Isaac Schwartz, Jacob Sloan and the Editor

The following songs are printed by special arrangement with the copyright holders: *Shabbat Hamalka* © 1966, Acum, Ltd., Tel Aviv, Israel; *Mi Y'malel?* © 1963, Israel Composers League Publishers, Ltd., Tel Aviv, Israel; *Ashrey Ha-Ish* © 1952, Merkaz Letarbut Vechinuch, Tel Aviv, Israel; *Bikurim* © 1960, Israel Composers League Publishers, Ltd., Tel Aviv, Israel; *Kru-im Anu* © 1951, A. Schlonsky; *Shir Eres* © 1966, Acum, Ltd., Tel Aviv, Israel; *Ali V'er (B'er)* © 1952, 1963, Israel Composers League Publishers, Ltd., Tel Aviv, Israel; *Shir Hakvish* © 1949, Merkaz Letarbut Vechinuch, Tel Aviv, Israel; *Shir Ha-Emek* © 1952, Daniel Sambursky; *Ruchot Hayam* © 1966, Acum, Ltd., Tel Aviv, Israel; *Artsa Alinu* © 1963, Merkaz Letarbut Vechinuch, Tel Aviv, Israel; *Se Ug'di* © 1958, Merkaz Letarbut Vechinuch, Tel Aviv, Israel; *Beyn N'har Prat* © 1966, Acum, Ltd., Tel Aviv, Israel; *Molad'ti* © 1966, Acum, Ltd., Tel Aviv, Israel; *Shir Ha-Palmach* © 1948, Hefer, Tel Aviv, Israel; *Zemer Lach* © 1948, Merkaz Letarbut Vechinuch, Tel Aviv, Israel; *Shir La-Negev* © 1961, Merkaz Letarbut Vechinuch, Tel Aviv, Israel; *Birkat Am (Tech'zakna)* © 1966, Acum, Ltd., Tel Aviv, Israel.

Third Printing, 1976

CONTENTS

SONGS OF LIFE AND WORK 77

HOLIDAY SONGS 139

SABBATH:

SUKKOT:

INTRODUCTION

JEWISH folk songs are as diverse and variegated as the Jews themselves. There are the songs of the Oriental Jews—Yemenite, Sephardic, Persian, Daghestanian, Babylonian, Moroccan; the Ladino songs of the Spaniolic Jews with their large collection of liturgical melodies; the Yiddish folk songs and hasidic tunes (with or without words) of the Eastern European Jews. The innumerable synagogal chants—religious folk songs—which differ one from the other depending upon the community in which they are current, are found among Jews the world over.

The youngest branch of this long line of Jewish folk songs is the Yiddish, which grew up and flourished, amid dire oppression and abject poverty, within the Pale of Settlement in czarist Russia of the nineteenth century. Yiddish folk songs constitute one of the richest stores of popular music of modern times.

The Yiddish folk song is a many-sided thing. It is the naive love song of a Jewish domestic in Rumania, and the lament of a seamstress in Lithuania; the plaintive chant of a lonely talmudic student of Galicia, and the cocky song of a thief of the Warsaw underworld. It is the gay wedding tune of White Russia and the Ukraine, and the lilting song of a Jewish journeyman of Odessa. It embraces cradle songs, children's songs, humorous and satiric songs, and the songs and ballads of the Jewish revolutionaries of czarist Russia; the *zemirot* and *niggunim* sung at the Sabbath meals, holiday songs, the songs of the pious Hasidim and of their opponents, the Mitnagdim, of the modern-minded Maskilim and of the freethinking Apikorsim; the songs of the merry-making *badchonim*, of the beggars, of the street singers, of the Yiddish theatre.

In these songs we catch the manner of speech, the wit and humor, dreams and aspirations, nonsense, jollity and pathos of a people. In them ring out fresh and clear the accents of a life which met with tragic destruction and is never to be recovered.

The mass migration to America of the Jews of Eastern Europe, in the

11

eighties and nineties of the last century, brought the Yiddish folk song to the New World; and that song became the basis for the new tunes created on American soil.

In the same period Jewish pioneers began to settle the land of Israel. Large sections of the present population of Israel originally came from Eastern Europe; many of the Hebrew folk songs which sprung up in that ancient land in the twentieth century echo in large measure the melodies, and often the words, of the Yiddish folk song of the previous century.

The Soviet Jewish community, remaining on Eastern European soil, also created a distinctive Yiddish folk song, based in large part upon the older Eastern European and hasidic tunes.

Then, in the dark years of the Nazi domination of Europe, a host of songs arose that record the heroic struggle of the Jewish people against the German overlord.

In the past decade, songs of battle and victory for the Jewish homeland have been added. The new setting of a young state on the soil of its ancient forefathers will undoubtedly give rise to songs of still another texture and color, thus enriching the whole body of Jewish song the world over.

The study of Jewish folk song represents a comparatively new field. This book is part of a larger effort toward the preservation of the cultural heritage of the Jewish people.

I wish gratefully to acknowledge the wise counsel and assistance given me by Nathan Ausubel, Norman Cazdan, Kalman Marmor, Shulamith Rabinovitch, and my husband, Harry Rubin.

R. R.

Pronunciation Guide

SOUND	EXAMPLE IN TEXT	ENGLISH EQUIVALENT	REMARKS
a	harts	heart	
e	ven	then	The _e_ is _always_ short and _always_ sounded.
i _or_	visn	drink	The difference in pronunciation between
	mir	beer	the two _i_'s is not indicated in the text.
o	hot	forgot	When two vowels are together, read
u	unter	room	them separately, as _tsien: tsi-en;_ or
oy	groys	boy	_toes: to-es;_ except for the diphthongs
ay	tayer	fire	_oy, ay, ey._
ey	freyd	way	

Except as indicated below, all consonants are the same as in English.

ch	chosn	Loch	guttural
g	gib	give	
ts	tants or tsores	huts	
tsh	mentsh	chair	
zh	shpil-zhe	seizure	
dz	undzer	sounds	

The pronunciation indicated for the Yiddish songs (with an occasional slight variation) follows in the main the Lithuanian manner of speech. As for the Hebrew songs, the Sephardic pronunciation current in Israel today is used, even in such songs as may have originated in Eastern Europe and were originally sung in the Ashkenazic pronunciation.

13

CRADLE SONGS

SOME of the oldest Yiddish folk songs of Eastern Europe are lullabies, which first made their appearance in the latter part of the Middle Ages. The dream of every Jewish mother is reflected in these tender, crooning songs. *Mayn kind vet lernen Toyre*, the basic aspiration of the entire people, runs through them like a golden thread. Parents endured great hardship so that their sons might be scholars. A lad with a *sharfn kepl* [keen mind] could even hope to marry the *nogid's* [rich man's] only daughter, though the average little Jewish town in the Pale often boasted no more than one *nogid*. However, the high regard for scholarship went deeper than the mere desire for economic security. The working mother, in making it possible for her son and husband to pursue their studies of the Torah, felt that she was not only achieving a strong position in the religious society of her day, but securing for herself a place in paradise as well.

Cradle songs were sung not only by the mother. Often the working mother had to call in a neighbor's child to "sit" with the baby, as in *Vigndig a fremd kind*. When the sitter had his or her own tale to tell, the lullaby took the form of *Amol is geven a mayse*. Even a father would occasionally compose a cradle song for his infant.

The eighties and nineties of the last century saw the rise of an organized movement of the workingmen and women of Eastern Europe. *Shlof mayn kind, shlof keseyder*, is a song of that period. In America, during the same years, masses of Jewish immigrants who had come over from Eastern Europe in search of *goldene glikn* [golden luck] in the *fraye medine* [free country] were being daily disillusioned by the stark reality of the sweatshops. *Mayn yingele*, written by the poet Morris Rosenfeld, who was himself a worker in a sweatshop, is a lullaby harking back to those years and is sung in several musical variants to the present day.

One of the most popular songs at the end of the nineteenth century was Sholom Aleichem's *Shlof mayn kind*, which gained a wide currency in the Eastern European Jewish communities before he even made it known that the text was his and the music David Kovanovski's.

Unter Dem Kind's Vigele

Un - ter dem kind's vi - ge - le Shteyt a klor - vays tsi - ge - le. Dos

tsi - ge - le z'ge - fo - rn hand - len Ro - zhin - kes mit

mand - len. Ro - hin - zkes mit mand - len iz zey - er zis.

Mayn kind vet zayn ge - zunt ___ un frish. ___

1 Unter dem kind's vigele
Shteyt a klor-vays tsigele.
Dos tsigele z'geforn handlen
Rozhinkes mit mandlen.
Rozhinkes mit mandlen iz zeyer zis.
Mayn kind vet zayn gezunt un frish.

2 Gezunt iz di beste schoyre.
Mayn kind vet lernen Toyre.
Toyre vet er lernen.
S'forim vet er shraybn.
A guter un a frumer
Vet er im yirtseshem blaybn.

1 Under baby's cradle here
There's an all-white nanny, dear.
Nanny's come to bring the baby
Almond nuts and raisin candy.
Raisins and nuts are a special treat.
Baby will grow up healthy and sweet.

2 Healthy's better far than wealthy.
Baby will grow up a scholar.
A scholar of the Torah will he be,
A writer too, of holy writs.
A good man and a pious,
God willing, that's what he will be.

Ay–Lye, Lyu–Lye, Lyu–Lye

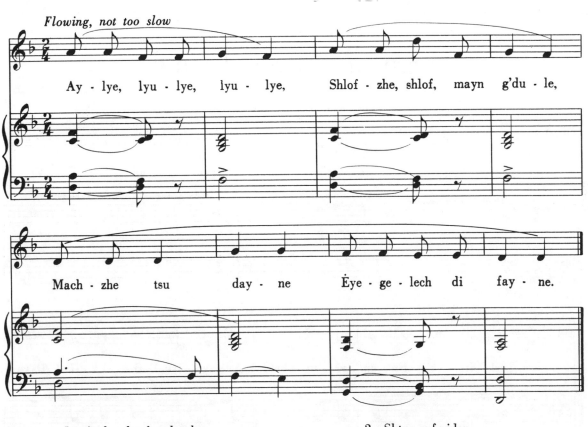

Flowing, not too slow

Ay - lye, lyu - lye, lyu - lye, Shlof - zhe, shlof, mayn g'du - le,

Mach - zhe tsu day - ne Eye - ge - lech di fay - ne.

1 Ay-lye, lyu-lye, lyu-lye,
Shlof-zhe, shlof, mayn g'dule,
Mach-zhe tsu dayne
Eygelech di fayne.

2 Shtey oyf vider,
Mit gezunte glider,
Mayn lib-zis kind
Gich un geshvind.

17

3   In mark vel ich loyfn,
    Beygelech vel ich koyfn.
    Mit puter vel ich shmirn—
    Tsu der chupe zol ich dich firn.

1   Ay-lye, lyu-lye, lyu-lye—
    Sleep, my pride and joy.
    Close your pretty eyes,
    Shut your pretty eyes.

2   When you wake up by and by,
    You will jump up fresh and spry.
    So sleep now, my baby dear,
    Tomorrow's very near.

4   Vest oysvaksn a groysinker,
    Vestu zayn a tane—
    Veln doch ale
    Zayn mich m'kane!

3   Then I'll hurry to the fair
    And I'll buy you fresh rolls there.
    And I'll butter them for you—
    And get a sweet bride for you, too.

4   You will grow up and be known
    For wisdom and piety.
    And then, every other mother
    Will be envious of me!

Vigndig A Fremd Kind

Zolst a-zoy le-bn un zayn ge-zint Vi ich __ vel dir zi-tsn un vi-gn s'kind. Ay-lyu-lyu, sha-sha-sha! Dayn

2nd time 8va

Chorus

18

ma - me - shi z'ge - gan - gen in mark a - rayn. Ay - lyu - lyu,

shlof mayn kind, Di ma - me - shi vet ki - men gich un ge - shvind.

1 Zolst azoy lebn un zayn gezint
Vi ich vel dir zitsn un vign s'kind.

Chorus:
   Ay-lyu-lyu, sha-sha-sha!
   Dayn mameshi z'gegangen in mark arayn.
   Ay-lyu-lyu, shlof mayn kind,
   Di mameshi vet kimen gich un geshvind.

2 Zolst azoy lebn, s'geyt mir derinen!
Dayn mameshi z'gegangen in mark arayn
    fardinen.

Chorus

3 Andere meydelech tantsn un shpringen
Un ich muz n'kind vign un zingen!

Chorus

4 Andere meydelech tsukerkelech nashn
Un ich muz n's'kind vindelech vashn!

Chorus

1 May you live long and be well, my lady,
While here I sit and rock your baby.

Ay-lyu-lyu, hush-hush-hush!
Your mother's gone to the marketplace.
Ay-lyu-lyu, hush-hush-hush,
Mama will soon back to you race.

2 Long may you live, for I wish it true,
Mama's gone to provide for you.

3 Other little girls can dance and swing,
But I must rock the baby and sing!

4 Other little girls can buy goodies and candies,
But I must wash the baby's panties!

19

Amol Iz Geven A Mayse

In ballad style

A - mol is ge - ven a may - se, Di may - se is gor - nit

frey - lech, Di may - se heybt zich o - net Mit a yi - di - shn mey - lech.

Chorus

Lyu - lin - ke mayn fey - ge - le Lyu - lin - ke mayn kind. Ch'ob

on - ge - voy - rn a - za li - be Vey iz mir un vind.

1   Amol is geven a mayse . . .
Di mayse iz gornit freylech—
Di mayse heybt zich onet
Mit a yidishn meylech.

Chorus:
  Lyulinke mayn feygele
  Lyulinke mayn kind.
Ch'ob ongevoyrn aza libe—
  Vey is mir un vind.

2   Der meylech hot gehat a malke,
Di malke hot gehat a vayngortn.
Der vayngortn hot gehat a boym.
Lyulinke mayn kind.

  Chorus

3   Der boym hot gehat a tsvayg.
Der tsvayg hot gehat a nestele,
Dos nestele hot gehat a feygele,
Lyulinke mayn kind.

  Chorus

4   Der meylech iz opgeshtorbn,
Di malke iz gevorn fardorbn.
Der tsvayg iz opgebrochn,
Dos feygele fun nest—antlofn.

  Chorus

5   Vu nemt men aza chochem
Der zol kenen di shtern tseyln?
Vu nemt men aza dokter
Er zol kenen mayn harts heyln?

  Chorus

Once upon a time there was . . .
Is the happy old beginning.
But our story's sad, and starts
With a Jewish king.

  Hush, my little birdie,
  Hush, my little baby.
  I have lost my own true love.
  Ah, woe is unto me!

2   The king he had a lovely queen,
The queen a vineyard fair had she.
The vineyard fair, it had a tree.
Hush, my little baby.

3   On the tree there was a branch,
On the branch there was a nest,
In the nest there was a birdie,
Hush, my little baby.

4   The king he died so suddenly,
The queen grew sad and pined away.
The branch broke off the tree, my love,
And the birdie flew away.

5   Where is there a wise man
Who can count the stars?
Where is there a doctor
Who can heal my heart?

Shlof Mayn Kind, Shlof Keseyder

1   Shlof mayn kind, shlof keseyder,
Zingen vel ich dir a lid.
Az du mayn kind, vest elter vern
Vestu visn an untershid.

2   Az du mayn kind, vest elter vern
Vestu vern mit laytn glaych.
Demolst vestu gevoyre vern
Vost heyst orim un vos heyst raych.

3   Di tayerste palatsn, di shenste hayzer,
Dos alts macht der oriman.
Nor veystu ver es tut in zey voynen?
Gor nisht er, nor der raycher man.

4   Der oriman, er ligt in keler,
Der vilgotsh rint im fun di vent.
Derfun bakumt er a rematn-feler
In di fis un in di hent.

1 Sleep my child, sleep,
I'll sing you a lullaby.
When my little baby's grown,
He'll know the difference—and why.

2 When my little baby's grown,
You'll soon see which is which.
Like the rest of us, you'll know
The difference between poor and rich.

3 The largest mansions, finest homes,
The poor man builds them on the hill.
But do you know, who'll live in them?
Why, of course, the rich man will!

4 The poor man lives in a cellar,
The walls are wet with damp.
He gets pains in his arms and legs
And a rheumatic cramp.

Shlof Mayn Kind

Text: Sholom Aleichem

Tune: David Kovanovski

Shlof mayn kind, mayn treyst mayn shey-ner, Shlof-zhe zu-ne-nyu,

Shlof mayn le-bn, mayn ka-dish ey-ner, Shlof-zhe, lyu-lyu-lyu.

Shlof mayn le-bn, mayn ka-dish ey-ner, Shlof-zhe, lyu-lyu-lyu.

1 Shlof mayn kind, mayn treyst mayn sheyner,
Shlof-zhe zunenyu,
Shlof mayn lebn, mayn kadish eyner,
Shlof-zhe, lyu-lyu-lyu.

2 Bay dayn vigl zitst dayn mame
Zingt a lid un veynt.
Du vest amol farshteyn mistame,
Vos zi hot gemeynt.

3 In Amerike iz der tate,
Däyner, zunenyu,
Du bizt noch a kind les-ate,
Shlof-zhe, lyu-lyu-lyu.

4 In Amerike iz far yedn,
Zogt men, gor a glik.
Un far yedn, a gan-eydn,
Gor epes an antik.

5 Dortn est men in der vochn
Chale, zunenyu,
Yaychelech vel ich dir kochn,
Shlof-zhe, lyu-lyu-lyu.

6 Er vet shikn tsvantsig doler,
Zayn portret dertsu,
Un vet nemen, lebn zol er!
undz ahintsutsu.

7 Er vet chapn undz un kushn,
Tantsn azh far freyd!
Ich vel kvaln trern gisn,
Veynen shtilerheyt.

8 Biz es kumt dos gute kvitl,
Shlof-zhe zunenyu,
Shlofn iz a tayer mitl,
Shlof-zhe, lyu-lyu-lyu.

1 Sleep my child, my consolation,
Sleep, sleep, lyu-lyu-lyu.
Sleep, my life, my adoration,
Sonny, sleep, lyu-lyu.

2 Your mother standing by your cradle
Crying, croons a lullaby.
Some day you may understand
Why your mother cries.

3 Your father's in America,
Far, far away—lyu-lyu.
Now you're but a little boy,
So sleep, my child, lyu-lyu.

4 In America, they say,
There is never any dearth.
It's a Paradise for all,
A real heaven on earth.

5 There they eat white bread, my darling,
All the whole week through.
I will cook hot broth for baby,
So go to sleep, lyu-lyu.

6 He will hug us then and kiss us,
He will dance for glee!
I shall shed tears, in a torrent,
Weeping silently.

7 God be willing, he will write us
Soon, soon, lyu-lyu-lyu.
And bring happiness to us
Sleep then, lyu-lyu-lyu.

8 Till the precious letter comes,
Sleep my child, lyu-lyu.
Sleep's a grand remedy,
Sleep, sleep, lyu-lyu-lyu.

Mayn Yingele

Text: Morris Rosenfeld

1 Ich hob a kleynem yingele,
A zunele gor fayn.
Ven ich derze im, dacht zich mir,
Di gantse velt iz mayn!

2 Nor zeltn, zeltn, ze ich im,
Mayn sheynem, ven er vacht.
Ich tref im imer shlofndig,
Ich ze im nor baynacht.

3 Di arbet traybt mich fri aroys,
Un lozt mich shpet tsurik.
O, fremd iz mir mayn eygn layb,
Mayn eygn kind's a blik.

4 Ich kum tsuklemterheyd aheym,
In finsternish gehilt,
Mayn bleyche froy dertseylt mir bald
Vi fayn dos kind zich shpilt.

5 Ich shtey bay zayn gelegerl,
Un her un ze un sha . . .
A troym bavegt di lipelech:
O, vu iz, vu iz Pa?

6 Ich kush di bloye oygelech
Zey efenen zich, o kind!
Zey ze-en mich, zey ze-en mich!
Un shlisn zich geshvind.

7 Do shteyt dayn Papa, tayerer,
A penele dir na!
A troym bavegt di lipelech:
O vu iz, vu iz Pa?

8 Ich blayb tsuveytogt un tsuklemt
Farbitert un ich kler:
Ven du ervachst amol, mayn kind,
Gefinstu mich nit mer.

I have a little boy, and whenever I see him, I think he is the finest little lad in the world. But it's seldom indeed that I see my son awake. At night when I come home from work, I always find him asleep. My work gets me up early in the morning and brings me home late at night. My son and I are strangers. I come home in low spirits. But my pallid wife tells me how nicely the child plays, how sweetly he prattles.

As I listen to her, my love for my son is awakened and I hurry in to see him. I stand near his crib and listen to his breathing, in silence. He is dreaming out loud: Where is Papa? I kiss his blue eyes. They open and see me! But then, quickly close again.

Darling! Here is your father, with a penny for you! But he is still dreaming out loud: Papa, where is Papa?

I turn pale with anguish, and embittered, think to myself: Some day when you wake up, my child, you'll find me gone forever.

Shlof Mayn Zun

Shlof mayn zun, mayn___ tay - er fey - ge - le, Mach di ey - ge - lech

Verse 5

Shlof mayn zun, mayn tay-er fey-ge-le, Mach di ey-ge-lech tsu.

Vest noch tsayt ho-bn tsu shti-fn Its-ter, shlof in dayn ru.

1 Shlof mayn zun, mayn tayer feygele,
Mach di eygelech tsu.
Vest noch tsayt hobn tsu shtifn,
Itster, shlof in dayn ru.

2 Ich vel dir koyfn sheyne shverdelech,
Mit a roytinker fon.
Du vest vaksn a gerotener,
Shlof mayn liber zun.

3 Shlof, mayn zun, mayn tayer feygele,
Shlof-zhe, shlof-zhe ayn.
Vest oysvaksn a groyser, a sheyninker,
Un a fli-er zayn!

4 Vestu fli-en in der vayt ahin,
Mit der zun baglaych.
Un ir vet zich beyde glikleche
Shpiglen inem taych.

5 *Same as first verse.*

28

1 Sleep my child, my baby chick,
Close your eyes, my son.
There will be time enough for play,
Sleep now, little one.

2 You shall have a sword, a bright red flag,
And many a pretty toy.
You will grow up a fine young man,
Sleep now, little **boy.**

3 Sleep my child, my little chick,
Sleep will come to you.
You'll grow up tall and handsome,
And be a pilot, too.

4 You will fly off into the distance,
Towards the sun you'll go.
You will both be happy, mirrored
In the lake below.

Yankele

"YANKELE" was written by Mordecai (Mordche) Gebirtig, favorite folk singer of the Polish Jews of our generation. He wrote this lullaby and many other such songs long before the Nazis overran his country and his town and led him to his death in 1942. Gebirtig's songs were as popular in Poland during the past quarter century as were the songs of Mark Warshavsky in Russia at the end of the 19th century. Their songs are in a sense comparable to those of Stephen Foster.

Text and tune: Mordche Gebirtig

Shlof - zhe mir shoyn, Yan - ke - le mayn shey - ner, Di
ey - ge - lech di shvarts - in - ke mach - tsu. A
yin - ge - le vos hot shoyn a - le tseyn - de - lech, Muz

1 Shlof-zhe mir shoyn, Yankele mayn sheyner,
Di eygelech di shvartsinke mach tsu.
A yingele vos hot shoyn ale tseyndelech
Muz noch di mame zingen: ay-lyu-lyu.

2 A yingele vos hot shoyn ale tseyndlech,
Un vet mit mazl bald in cheyder geyn,
Un lernen vet er, chumesh un gemore,
Zol veynen ven di mame vigt im ayn?

3 A yingele vos lernen vet gemore,
Ot shteyt der tate, kvelt un hert zich tsu.
A yingele vos vakst a talmid-chochem,
Lozt gantse necht der mamen nit tsuru?

4 A yingele vos vakst a talmid-chochem,
Un a geniter soycher oych tsuglaych.
A yingele, a kluger chosn-bocher,
Zol lign azoy nas, vi in a taych?

5 Nu shlof-zhe mir, mayn kluger chosn-bocher—
Dervayl ligstu in vigele bay mir—
S'vet kostn noch fil mi un mame's trern,
Bizvanen s'vet a mentsh aroys fun dir!

31

1 Sleep, Yankele, my darling little baby,
Shut your big black eyes.
A big boy who has all his teeth,
Ought Mother sing him lullabies?

2 A big boy who has all his teeth,
And will go to school by and by,
And study Torah and Gemara,
Ought he, when his mother rocks him, cry?

3 A big boy who soon will study Gemara,
While father stands by, nodding happily.
A big boy, who's growing up a scholar,
Ought he nights not let his mother be?

4 A big boy growing up a scholar,
And an enterprising merchant yet.
A big boy who will make a nice girl happy,
Ought he to be lying here so wet?

5 Sleep then, sleep, my groom that is to be,
Right now you're in the cradle, sad but true—
It will cost much toil and many tears,
Before anything becomes of you!

CHILDREN'S SONGS

A CHILD's life in Eastern Europe a hundred years ago was not a carefree one. Boys were sent (or rather brought) to *cheder* [school] very early, often at the age of four and five. (Girls did not go to *cheder*.) During the long winter months the roads were snow-covered and sleety and it was hazardous for little children to go alone. So they would be carried pickaback by the *behelfer*, the *melamed's* [teacher's] assistant. A boy usually went to *cheder* until he was of marriageable age. Then the marriage contract would be drawn up and the boy would in most cases go to live with his in-laws, continuing his studies there. A typical household of those days would show a troop of younger children under the care of an older sister, with the mother away earning a livelihood, and the father, together with the boys, poring over the Torah in the House of Study.

In other respects the children of the Jewish Pale were not too different from children in other parts of the world. They composed ditties, songs, taunts, nonsense rhymes and chants in great number.

> *Enge, benge, stupe, stenge,*
> *Artse, bartse, gole shvartse,*
> *Eymele, reymele, beygele, feygele, hop!*

is one version of a counting song that might be compared with the American "Eenie, meenie, mynie, moe." Blindman's buff was played to the chant of

> *Hotzmach iz a blinder,*
> *Vu zenen zayne kinder,*
> *Hotzmach is a blinder!*
> *Ot zenen mir ale do!*

The six songs given here represent six different types of children's songs, but by no means all the types: the narrative song, *Bay dem shtetl*; the game song, *Treti, treti, treti*; the cumulative, house-that-Jack-built type of song, *Funem sheynem vortsl aroys*; the nonsense song, *Hob ich a por oksn*, which is also a cumulative song; the musical instrument song, *Hob ich mir a kleynem Michalke*; and the riddle song, *Du meydele du sheyns*, which is a children's variant of an adult riddle song of the same name. The riddle

33

song anciently did duty as a courting song as well, and such an example is to be found in the Songs of Life and Work (*Nem aroys a ber fun vald*).

Treti, treti, treti, may be likened to the English-American "Go in and out the window"; *Funem sheynem vortsl aroys* can similarly be compared to the English "And the green grass growing all around, all around."

Curiously, the song *Hob ich a por oksn,* although it builds upon nonsense rhymes, yet manages to have the various animals mentioned perform tasks that reflect the routine in the Jewish Pale of a century ago: *lokshn* [noodles] are made, kindling wood is gathered, the house is swept clean, babies are rocked to sleep, *beygel* are baked in the oven, and one's own supply of ink is made right at home.

Bay Dem Shtetl

1 Bay dem shtetl shteyt a shtibl
Mit a grinem dach.
Un arum dem shtibl vaksn
Beymelech a sach.

2 Un der tate un di mame
Chanele mit mir,
Shoyn a lange tsayt ineynem
Voynen ale fir.

3 Un der tate horevet, horevet,
Ale yorn zayne,
Un er koyft undz un er brengt undz
Zachn sheyne, fayne!

4 Brengt a hintl vos se havket,
Mitn nomen Tsutsik.
Brengt a ferdl vos se hirzhet,
Mitn nomen Mutsik.

5 Brengt a gandz mit a langn haldz,
Federlech vays vi shney,
Brengt a hun vos kvoket, kvoket,
Biz zi leygt an ey!

6 Nemt di mame, ot di eyer,
Oy, iz dos a moyfes!
Zetst zi oyf oyf zey a kvoke:
Hobn mir sheyne oyfes!

1 There's a hut on the edge of town
And its roof is green.
And all around the hut
Trees are to be seen.

2 And my father and my mother,
My sister Chanele and me,
We have all been living here
A long time, happily.

35

3 Oh, how hard my father works.
Winter, summer, fall and spring!
Yet whenever he comes home,
He brings us gifts and things!

4 Bringing a puppy dog that barks,
And its name is Tsutsik.
Bringing a little pony that neighs,
And its name is Mutsik.

5 Bringing a goose with a long white throat,
Snow-white feathers and white legs.
Bringing a hen that cackle-cackles,
When she is laying eggs.

6 Then my mother takes the eggs
And sets them under a setting-hen.
And—miracles of miracles—
We have baby chickens then!

Hob Ich A Por Oksn

Hob ich a por ok - sn, ok - sn Vos zey bro - kn
lok - shn, lok - shn, Ay, vun - der i - ber vun - der,
Vi di ok - sn bro - kn lok - shn, Dos iz mir a

*The additional lines in the remaining verses are sung to this measure.

36

vun - der,   dos iz mir a vun - der.

1 Hob ich a por oksn, oksn
Vos zey brokn lokshn, lokshn,
Ay, vunder iber vunder,
Vi di oksn brokn lokshn,
Dos iz mir a vunder, dos iz mir a vunder.

2 Hob ich a por bern, bern,
Vos zey shtiber kern, kern.
Ay, vunder iber vunder,
Vi di bern shtiber kern,
Un di oksn brokn lokshn, *etc.*

3 Hob ich a por tsign, tsign,
Vos zey kinder vign, vign.
Ay, vunder iber vunder,
Vi di tsign kinder vign,
Un di bern shtiber kern, *etc.*

4 Hob ich a por hint, hint,
Vos zey machn tint, tint.
Ay, vunder iber vunder,
Vi di hint machn tint,
Un di tsign kinder vign, *etc.*

5 Hob ich a por hener, hener,
Vos zey klaybn shpener, shpener.
Ay, vunder iber vunder,
Vi di hener klaybn shpener,
Un di hint machn tint, *etc.*

6 Hob ich a por feygelech, feygelech,
Vos zey bakn beygelech, beygelech.
Ay, vunder iber vunder,
Vi di feygelech bakn beygelech,
Un di hener klaybn shpener,
Un di hint machn tint,
Un di tsign kinder vign,
Un di bern shtiber kern,
Un di oksn brokn lokshn,
Dos iz mir a vunder, dos iz mir a vunder.

1 I've a pair of poodles, poodles,
And they're chopping noodles, noodles.
Miracle of miracles!
See the poodles chopping noodles.
There's a miracle!

2 I've a pair of sables, sables,
And they're dusting tables, tables.
Miracle of miracles!
See the sables dusting tables,
See the poodles chopping noodles, *etc.*

3 I've a pair of kittens, kittens,
And they're knitting mittens, mittens.
Miracle of miracles!
See the kittens knitting mittens,
See the sables dusting tables, *etc.*

4 I've a pair of lynx, lynx,
And they're mixing inks, inks,
Miracle of miracles!
See the lynx mixing inks,
See the kittens knitting mittens, *etc.*

5 I've a pair of turtles, turtles,
And they're picking myrtles, myrtles.
Miracle of miracles!
See the turtles picking myrtles,
See the lynx mixing inks, *etc.*

6 I've a pair of moles, moles
And they're baking rolls, rolls,
Miracle of miracles!
See the moles baking rolls,
See the turtles picking myrtles,
See the lynx mixing inks,
See the kittens knitting mittens,
See the sables dusting tables,
See the poodles chopping noodles.
There's a miracle!

Treti, Treti, Treti

All the little girls stand in a ring, holding hands. Sore stands alone in the center, singing aloud, together with all the other little girls. When the part *in dray yor arum* comes, Sore, in a "dignified" manner, turns around slowly, three times, with eyes closed, one arm outstretched and finger pointing. When she makes her third complete turn, she stops and the one she is pointing at—in this instance Chaye—is the next one to stand in the center of the ring.

This is obviously a song composed by very young children, as is plain from the ungrammatical first four lines. *Vos in Treti zang?* might mean "What is the Treti song?" or "What is sung in the land of Treti?" or "How is music made in Treti?" In any case music is brought by a beautiful bird. Then follows the solemn ritual of choosing a mate, found in so many children's games (as in the American and English "Bluebird, Bluebird Through My Window" or even indirectly in "The Farmer in the Dell" and others). Here, however, it is foretold that "three years from now" the one so chosen will be "turning around"—turning around, undoubtedly, under the canopy.

Hot ge-zun-gen, hot ge-zun-gen, In dray yor a-rum

Dreyt zich So-re a-rum. So-re hot zich a-rum-ge-dreyt Cha-ye hot zich dem kopf far-dreyt.

Treti, treti, treti,
Vos in Treti zang?
Kumt a sheyner foygl
Un macht a sheyn gezang.
Hot gezungen, hot gezungen,
In dray yor arum
Dreyt zich Sore arum.

Chanted:
  Sore hot zich arumgedreyt
  Chaye hot zich dem kop fardreyt.

Treti, treti, treti,
Vos in Treti zang?
Kumt a sheyner foygl
Un macht a sheyn gezang.
Hot gezungen, hot gezungen,
In dray yor arum
Dreyt zich Chaye arum.

Chanted:
  Chaye hot zich arumgedreyt
  Beyle hot zich dem kop fardreyt.

Treti, treti, treti,
What's the Treti song?
A pretty bird came flying
With the Treti song.
Singing this pretty round:
Three years from this day
Sarah will be turning round.

Sarah has turned all around—
Chaye's head is spinning now.

Treti, treti, treti,
What's the Treti song?
A pretty bird came flying
With the Treti song.
Singing this pretty round:
Three years from this day
Chaye will be turning round.

Chaye has turned all around—
Beyle's head is spinning now.

Hob Ich Mir A Kleynem Michalke

In this game song the children play the part of members of an orchestra. The friend Michalke is the leader of the game; as he completes his instruments he also chooses the one to play it.

As soon as one is picked, he walks round and round the ring of singing children, who imitate him and his instrument. In this song five instruments are mentioned. Many more of course can be added.

With each game a new Michalke is selected.

fay - fe - le. Dos fay - fe - le macht a - zoy: Flu- flu- flu,

flu - flu - flu, _____ A - zoy macht dos fay - fe - le.

Chorus:

Hob ich mir a kleynem Michalke, Michalke, ,
Voynt er oyf der langer gas.
Macht er mir vos ich vil.
Macht er mir vos er kon.

1 Macht er mir a fayfele.
Dos fayfele macht azoy:
Flu-flu-flu, flu-flu-flu,
Azoy macht dos fayfele.

Chorus

2 Macht er mir a trubetska,
Dos trubetske macht azoy:
Tru-tru-tru, tru-tru-tru,
Azoy macht dos trubetske,
Flu-flu-flu, flu-flu-flu, *etc.*

Chorus

3 Macht er mir a paykele,
Dos paykele macht azoy:
Tarabam-bam-bam, tarabam-bam-bam,
Azoy macht dos paykele,
Tru-tru-tru, tru-tru-tru, *etc.*

Chorus

4 Macht er mir a fidele,
Dos fidele macht azoy:
Tidl-tidl-tidl, tidl-tidl-tidl,
Azoy macht dos fidele,
Tarabam-bam-bam, tarabam-bam-bam, *etc.*

Chorus

5 Macht er mir a tsimbele,
Dos tsimbele macht azoy:
Tsim-tsim-tsim, tsim-tsim-tsim,
Azoy macht dos tsimbele,
Tidl-tidl-tidl, tidl-tidl-tidl,
Azoy macht dos fidele,
Tarabam-bam-bam, tarabam-bam-bam,
Azoy macht dos paykele,
Tru-tru-tru, tru-tru-tru,
Azoy macht dos trubetske,
Flu-flu-flu, flu-flu-flu,
Azoy macht dos fayfele!

*The additional lines in the remaining verses are sung to these last four measures.

41

I've a friend called Michalke, Michalke,
He lives on that long, long street.
He can make most anything,
And he makes me everything.

1 He makes for me a whistle,
The whistle goes like this:
Flu-flu-flu, flu-flu-flu,
That is how the whistle goes.

2 He makes for me a bugle,
The bugle goes like this:
Tru-tru-tru, tru-tru-tru,
This is how the bugle goes.

3 He makes for me a drum,
The drum, it goes like this:
Tarabam-bam-bam, tarabam-bam-bam,
This is how the drum goes.

4 He makes for me a fiddle,
This is how the fiddle goes:
Tidl-tidl-tidl, tidl-tidl-tidl,
This is how the fiddle goes.

5 He makes for me a triangle,
The triangle goes like this:
Tsim-tsim-tsim, tsim-tsim-tsim,
This is how the triangle goes.

Funem Sheynem Vortsl Aroys

This song, like *Hob ich a por oksn*, also serves as a "tongue-twister" and is sung faster as the song accumulates.

*The additional lines in the remaining verses are sung to this measure.

42

vor · tsl fun der erd. Zint s'iz ba · sha · fn hi · ml un erd.

1 Funem sheynem vortsl aroys
Iz a sheyner boym aroys.
Boym funem vortsl, vortsl fun der erd.
Zint s'iz bashafn himl un erd.

2 Funem sheynem boym aroys
Iz a sheyner tsvayg aroys.
Tsvayg funem boym, boym funem vortsl, *etc.*

3 Funem sheynem tsvayg aroys
Is a sheyner nest aroys.
Nest funem tsvayg, tsvayg funem boym, *etc.*

4 Funem sheynem nest aroys
Iz a sheyner foygl aroys.
Foygl funem nest, nest funem tsvayg, *etc.*

5 Funem sheynem foygl aroys
Iz a sheyner feder aroys.
Feder funem foygl, foygl funem nest, *etc.*

6 Funem sheynem feder aroys
Iz a guter kishn aroys.
Kishn funem feder, feder funem foygl,
Foygl funem nest, nest funem tsvayg,
Tsvayg funem boym, boym funem vortsl,
Vortsl fun der erd.
Zint s'iz bashafn himl un erd.

1 Out of the lovely root
Grew a lovely tree.
Tree out of root, root out of earth,
Ever since God created heaven and earth.

2 Out of the lovely tree
Grew a lovely limb.
Limb out of tree, tree out of root, *etc.*

3 Out of the lovely limb
Came a lovely nest.
Nest out of limb, limb out of tree, *etc.*

4 Out of the lovely nest
Came a lovely bird.
Bird out of nest, nest out of limb, *etc.*

5 Out of the lovely bird
Came a lovely feather.
Feather out of bird, bird out of nest, *etc.*

6 Out of the lovely feather
Came a fine pillow.
Pillow out of feather, feather out of bird,
Bird out of nest, nest out of limb,
Limb out of tree, tree out of root,
Root out of earth,
Ever since God created heaven and earth.

Du Meydele Du Sheyns

Du mey-de-le du fayns, du mey-de-le du sheyns

Ich vel dir e-pes fre-gn: a re-ten-ish a kleyns:

Vos iz he-cher fun ___ a hoyz?

Vos iz ___ flin-ker fun ___ a moyz?

1 Du meydele du fayns, du meydele du sheyns
Ich vel dir epes fregn: a retenish a kleyns:
Vos iz hecher fun a hoyz?
Vos iz flinker fun a moyz?

2 Du narisher bocher, du narisher chlop!
Host doch nit kayn seychl in dayn kop!
Der roych iz hecher fun a hoyz,
A katz is flinker fun a moyz.

3 Du meydele du fayns, du meydele du sheyns,
Ich vel dir epes fregn, a retenish a kleyns:
Vos flit on fligl?
Vos moyert on tsigl?

4 Du narisher bocher, du narisher chlop!
Host doch nit kayn seychl in dayn kop!
Shney flit on fligl.
Der frost moyert on tsigl.

5 Du meydele du fayns, du meydele du sheyns,
Ich vel dir epes fregn, a retenish a kleyns:
Vos fara keyser iz on a land?
Vos fara vaser iz on zamd?

6 Du narisher bocher, du narisher chlop!
Host doch nit kayn seychl in dayn kop!
Der keyser fun kortn iz on a land.
Trern fun di oygn iz on zamd.

1 Maid so pretty, maid so little,
Let me ask you a very hard riddle:
What is higher than a house?
What is quicker than a mouse?

2 You silly fellow, you cockadoodle,
You've no brains at all in your noodle!
Smoke is higher than a house.
A cat is quicker than a mouse.

3 Maid so pretty, maid so little,
Let me ask you a very hard riddle:
What falls without sound?
What builds on no ground?

4 You silly fellow, you cockadoodle,
You've no brains at all in your noodle!
Snow falls without sound.
Frost builds on no ground.

5 Maid so pretty, maid so little,
Let me ask you a very hard riddle:
What king has no land?
What water has no sand?

6 You silly fellow, you cockadoodle,
You've no brains at all in your noodle!
The king of spades has no land.
A maiden's tears have no sand.

LOVE SONGS

To DREAM of love, let alone sing of it, was considered alien and sinful in the Jewish Pale of a hundred years ago. *Yiches* [social standing], *nadan* [dowry], *tachlis* [economic security], *lomdes* [knowledge of the Torah]— these were the deciding factors in the selecting of a mate. The parents decided for the child upon its future wife or husband.

For this reason the average Jewish boy or girl of that day was deprived of a normal adolescence. Naturally, too, some unhappy marriages resulted, which are reflected in a type of love song that expresses longing, sorrow, frustration. The young people, if they fell in love, did so on the sly and were compelled to conceal their emotions. Often a young girl in desperation would take her mother into her confidence, pleading with her to arrange a match for her with the one she loved so dearly. This is vividly expressed in the song *Mamenyu, lyubenyu.*

Since falling in love without benefit of parents or marriage-brokers was frowned upon, the older songs are couched in simple and often naive terms. Nevertheless, the tunes remain poignant and expressive, as in *Tif in veldele.* Sometimes this is reversed and the words achieve a measure of poetic quality, whereas the tune weaves in and out like the chants of the talmudic students, as in *Indroysn is a triber tog.*

The expulsions of entire communities from their homes, harsh military laws, the constant quest for a livelihood, caused the breaking up of many love affairs and even of the established homes of young married couples. The theme of separation, of parting, is prominent in many songs, as in *Dortn, dortn, ibern vaserl.*

The general state of economic insecurity compelled many mothers to send their daughters into "service" in the homes of the wealthy. These domestics were probably the first carriers of songs from one community to another. It did not take long for the songs to "catch on," since they also answered to the yearnings of the girls of "better" homes, who "sat and crocheted" while quietly weeping tears of longing for a lover.

With the entry of the women of Eastern Europe into industry at the end of the nineteenth century, we come upon many love songs composed by seamstresses. In them they bewailed their unhappy lot, their life of hard work and social degradation. As working girls, lacking a dowry, they were usually destined to lonely spinsters' lives, and often, too, fell victim to some young rake. Faithless or unrequited love is the theme of many of the songs composed at that time, as in *Tsvey taybelech*, or *Ich hob ge-akert un gezeyt*.

Side by side with the many songs of sorrow, a large number of gay, mischievous and even naughty songs of love were created. These have an exceedingly charming and idyllic quality, as in *Zits ich mir oyfn benkele*, or *Di mame is gegangen in mark arayn*. Often, to escape the constant interference of parents, so well expressed in *Di fayerdige libe*, young people would take matters into their own hands and elope, not only to another city, but even much farther, to America.

Seen as a whole, the Yiddish love songs of a century ago served as a means of indirect protest against life in the Pale. They served to express feelings which society otherwise neither provided for nor countenanced. Perhaps that is why the love song, more than any other category of Yiddish folk song, achieved the greatest measure of poetic beauty and was able to inspire the generation of Yiddish poets which emerged at the end of the nineteenth century.

Tif In Veldele

With deep longing

Tif in vel - de - le shteyt___ a bey - me - le Un di tsvay - ge - lech bli - en. Un bay mir,___ o - rim shnay - der - l, Tut mayn her - tse - le tsi - en.

2   Oyfn beymele vakst a tsvaygele
Un di bletelech tsviten.
Un mayn orim shvach hertsele
Tsit tsu mayn ziser Iten.

3   Oyfn tsvaygele shteyt a feygele
Un dos feygele pishtshet.
Un bay mir, orim shnayderl,
Mayn shvach hertsele trishtshet.

1 Deep in the heart of the forest
A young tree is leaving.
And my poor tailor's heart
Heavily is grieving.

2 On the tree a branch is sprouting
And the leaves are blooming.
And my soft faint heart
Pines for my darling.

3 On the branch in the heart of the forest
There's a chirping bird.
And my poor tailor's heart
Bursts here, all unheard.

49

Mamenyu, Lyubenyu

2   Ich hob zich ayngelibt in a sheyn ingele
Sheyn vi a rendl gold.
Im mamenyu hob ich gelibt,
Un im hob ich take gevolt.

3   Shpatsirn zenen mir beyde gegangen
Arum un arum dem bulvar.
Ale meydelech shpiln libes—
Un ich bin geblibn tsum nar.

4   A cholem tatenyu, a cholem mamenyu
A cholem hot zich mir gedacht
Zayne sheyne bekelech mit di shvartse eygelech
Hobn mich krank gemacht.

5   Mayne tsores hobn mich arumgeringlt
Azoy vi a bonder a fas.
Hayntige yingelech iz azoyfil tsu gloybn
Azoy vi dem hunt oyfn gas!

1   Mother, dear mother, stand by me now,
Hear my pitiful plea.
Put out the fire that burns in my heart
And get whom I want—for me.

2   I've fallen in love with a handsome lad
Who shines like the midday sun.
Oh, mother dear, it's him that I love,
He's the only possible one.

3   We two often went walking
Around and around the park.
I really loved him truly,
But for him 'twas but a lark!

4   Was it a dream, O father, O mother?
Was it all a dream on my part?
His smooth cheeks and black eyes so tender
Have broken my yearning heart.

5   My troubles circle me round about,
My desolation is complete.
The lads of today can be trusted
No more than the dogs on the street!

51

Zits Ich Mir Oyfn Benkele

1 Zits ich mir oyfn benkele
Un farkem mir mayne herelech,
Geyt farbay, oy, a shnayder-yung
Un zogt az ich bin nit erlech.

2 Er zogt: as s'iz tint,
Un ich zog az s'iz penes.
Er zogt az her hot mich lib,
Un ich zog az s'iz nit emes!

3 Zits ich mir oyfn fensterl
Un farflecht mir mayne tsepelech,
Geyt farbay, oy, a shuster-yung
Un zogt az ich bin nit erlech.

4 Er zogt, az s'iz ash,
Un ich zog as s'iz koyln.
Er zogt az er vet mich nemen—
Un ich zog: er vet nit poyln!

1 Sitting on the bench,
Combing out my hair,
A tailor boy he passes by
And says I am not fair.

2 He says: It is dyed,
And I say: No, it's blue.
He says he loves me dear,
I say that is not true!

3 Sitting on the window sill,
Braiding my long hair,
A cobbler boy he passes by
And says I am not fair.

4 He says: It's ash-gray,
I say: It is coal-black.
He says that he will marry me—
I say: But that will never be!

Oy, Dortn, Dortn, Ibern Vaserl

Oy, dor·tn, dor·tn, i·bern va·se·rl Oy, dor·tn, dor·

tn, i·bern__brik._____ Far·tri·bn hos·tu mich in di

vay·te·ne len·der Un ben·ken benk__ich noch dir tsu·rik.___

2 Oy helf mir Gotenyu, oy Got in himl,
Oy helf mir Gotenyu, s'iz mir nit gut,
Shoyn tsayt dray yorelech vi mir shpiln a libe
Un oys-shpiln di libe konen mir nit.

3 Oy dayne oygelech, vi di shvartse kershelech
Un dayne lipelech, vi rozeve papir,
Un dayne fingerlech, vi tint un feder.
Oy, shraybn zolstu ofte briv tsu mir!

1 Far off, far off, across the bridge,
Far off, across the river blue,
You have driven me, far, far away
Yet I still long for you.

2 ·Oh help me, God, oh God in heaven,
Oh help me, God, for I am ill.
Three whole years we've played at love
But never loved, and play on still.

3 Oh, your eyes, like cherries black,
And your lips—a rosy moon,
And your fingers—pen and ink.
Oh, write to me often—and write soon!

Di Mame Iz Gegangen

Playful

Di ma-me is ge-gan-gen in mark a-rayn noch koy-ln,

(Repeat two octaves higher)

Hot zi mir ge-bracht_____ a yin-ge-le fun Poy-ln.

Ay iz dos a yin-ge-le, a sheyns__ un a fayns,

Mit di shvar-tse ey - ge-lech, ket-se-le du mayns!

2 Di mame iz gegangen ın mark arayn noch kroyt,
Hot zi mir gebracht a yingele fun boyd.
Ay iz dos a yingele, a sheyns un a fayns—
Mit di vayse tseyndelech, ketsele du mayns!

3 Ich hob gegesn mandlen, ich hob getrunken vayn,
Ich hob gelibt a yingele, un kon on im nit zayn.
Ay iz dos a yingele, a sheyns un a fayns—
Mit di shvartse herelech, ketsele du mayns!

1 My mother went to market for to buy some coal,
She brought me back a handsome lad from Poland.
Oh what a lad he is, how manly and how fine—
Ah those black eyes of his, ah, that kitten of mine!

2 My mother went to market for to buy some cabbage,
She brought me back a handsome lad, just off the coach.
Oh what a lad he is, how manly and how fine—
Ah those white teeth of his, ah, that kitten of mine!

3 I've been eating almonds, I've been drinking wine,
I'm in love with a handsome lad, and for him I pine.
Oh what a lad he is, how manly and how fine—
Ah those black curls of his, ah, that kitten of mine!

Papir Iz Doch Vays

Pa - pir iz doch vays____ un____ tint iz doch shvarts, Tzu

dir mayn zis____ le - bn, tsit____ doch mayn harts. Ich volt

shten - dig ge - ze - sn dray teg____ noch - an - and Tsu

ku - shn dayn sheyn____ po - ním un tsu hal - tn dayn hant.

1 Papir iz doch vays un tint iz doch shvarts,
Tsu dir mayn zis lebn, tsit doch mayn harts.
Ich volt shtendig gezesn dray teg nochanand
Tsu kushn dayn sheyn ponim un tsu haltn dayn
hant.

2 Nechtn baynacht bin ich oyf a chasene geven,
Fil sheyne meydelech hob ich dort gezen.
Fil sheyne meydelech—tsu dir kumt nisht gor—
Mit dayne shvartse eygelech un dayne shvartse
hor.

3 Dayn talye, dayn mi-ne, dayn eydeler fason,
In hartsn brent a fayer, men zet es nit on.
Nito aza mentsh, vos zol filn vi es brent,
Der toyt un dos lebn iz bay Got in di hent.

4 Ach du liber Got, her oys mayn farlang,
Dem oysher gistu kovid, mit a sheynem gang—
Oy, mir, gib a shtibele oyf dem groz dem grinem
Az ich mit mayn zis-lebn zoln voynen derinen.

1 Oh, paper is white, and ink is black or blue,
My own sweet life, my heart goes out to you.
Oh, I could sit forever, forever at your side,
Kissing your sweet face and wishing you my bride.

2 Yesterday I went to a wedding fair,
Many, many pretty girls did I see there.
Many, many pretty girls, but not a one like you,
With your black hair and your eyes of pitch-black hue.

3 Your figure, your manner, your gentility,
There's a fire in my heart that no one can see.
Nobody can guess what's in this heart of mine,
Life and death—lie in God's hands divine.

4 Oh, dear Lord, do listen to my plea,
To the rich you've granted splendor and finery—
To me, oh, give a hut upon the grass so green
That I and my own true love may together dwell therein.

Tum–Balalayka

Shteyt a bo - cher un___ er tracht Tracht un

tracht a gan - tze nacht: Ve - men tsu ne - men un nit far -

she - men? Ve - men tsu ne - men un nit far - she - men?

Tum - ba - la, tum - ba - la, tum - ba - la - lay - ka Tum - ba - la,

tum - ba - la, tum - ba - la - lay - ka Tum - ba - la - lay - ka, shpil ba - la -

lay - ka, Tum - ba - la - lay - ka, shpil ba - la - lay - ka.

1   Shteyt a bocher un er tracht
Tracht un tracht a gantse nacht:
Vemen tsu nemen un nit farshemen?
Vemen tsu nemen un nit farshemen?

Chorus:

Tum-bala, tum-bala, tum-balalayka
Tum-bala, tum-bala, tum-balalayka
Tum-balalayka, shpil balalayka.
Tum-balalayka, shpil balalayka.

2   Meydl, meydl, ch've' bey dir fregn:
Vos kon vaksn, vaksn on regn?
Vos kon brenen un nit oyfhern?
Vos kon benken, veynen on trern?

Chorus

3   Narisher bocher, vos darfstu fregn?
A shteyn kon vaksn, vaksn on regn.
Libe kon brenen, un nit oyfhern.
A harts kon benken, veynen on trern.

Chorus

1   A lad stood thinking all the night through,
Thinking, thinking, what to do?
Whose heart to take? Whose heart not to break?
Whose heart to take? Whose heart not to break?

Tum-bala, tum-bala, tum-balalayka,
Tum-bala, tum-bala, tum-balalayka
Tum-balalayka, strum balalayka.
Tum-balalayka, strum balalayka.

2   Maiden, maiden, tell me true,
What can grow, grow without dew?
What can burn for years and years?
What can cry and shed no tears?

3   Silly lad, here's the answer true:
A stone can grow, grow without dew.
Love can burn for years and years.
A heart can cry and shed no tears.

59

Ich Hob Ge–akert Un Gezeyt

With bitterness

Right hand may be omitted

Ich hob ge-a-kert un ge-zeyt ___ K' dey mayn tvu-e zol nit bre-nen. Un ver es hot mich fun mayn tay-er le-bn tsu-sheyt ___ Dem ___ zol di erd nit tsu-nem-en!

2 Er iz tsu mir arayngekumen,
Er iz gevezn mayn lebn,
Dos shenste perele fun dem tsvaygele
Hob ich im avekgegebn.

3 Er iz tsu mir arayngekumen,
Ich hob im gelibt vi mayn lebn;
Dos shenste tsvaygele fun dem boymele
Hob ich im avekgegebn.

1 I have plowed and I have sowed
Deep, that my crop might thrive.
Now may the earth deny that man
Who tore my dear love from my side!

2 My love he came to me,
He was my very life.
The fairest pearl upon the branch
I gave to him I love.

3 My love he came to me,
I loved him as my life.
The fairest branch upon the tree
I gave to him I love.

Di Fayerdige Libe

With flowing rhythm

no pedal

Di fay-er-di-ge li-be, Zi tut in har-tsn bre-nen. Oy, zi-ser Got, du veyst dem e-mes, As mir ko-nen zich nit ne-men.

2 Shuldig iz dayn tate,
Shuldig iz dayn mame,
Un du aleyn, mayn tayer lebn,
Bist shuldig mer fun ale.

3 Oyf morgn inderfri,
Der pastuch blozt zayn horn,
Ich mit dir, mayn tayer lebn,
Antlofn gevorn.

4 In a fremder shtot,
Tsvishn fremde mentshn,
Ver vet undz tsu der chupe firn?
Un ver vet undz bentshn?

5 In a fremder shtot,
Tvishn fremde mentshn,
Zey veln undz tsu der chupe firn
Un Got vet undz bentshn.

1 There is a burning in
My heart and in my head.
Oh, sweet God, you know the truth,
Why we cannot wed.

2 Your father is to blame,
Your mother is to blame,
And more than they, dear life,
You are to blame.

3 Early in the morning,
When the shepherd blows his horn,
Let us two, my own dear life,
Run off and be gone!

4 In a strange city,
In stranger's company,
Who will say the blessing?
Who hold the canopy?

5 In a strange city,
In stranger's company,
God will say the blessing
Under the canopy.

Oyfn Oyvn Zitst A Meydl

(The refrain "Tumba, tumba, tum-ba-ba" is sung after each line of the text.)

Oy - fn oy - vn zitst a mey - dl
Iz a bo - cher on - ge - floy - gn,
Tum - ba, tum - ba, tum - ba - ba

Un zi heft a zay - dn kley - dl.
Un hot dem fo - dim op - ge - tsoy - gn.
Tum - ba, tum - ba, tum - ba - ba

Ay du bo - cher, ay du fay - er!__ Tum - ba, tum - ba, tum - ba ba

S'vet dich kos - tn zey - er tay - er.__ Tum - ba, tum - ba, tum - ba - ba

62

Oyfn oyvn zitst a meydl
Un zi heft a zaydn kleydl.
Iz a bocher ongefloygn,
Un hot dem fodim opgetsoygn.

Ay du bocher, ay du fayer!
S'vet dich kostn zeyer tayer.

Nit mit shtrik vel ich dich penten
Nor mit mayne vayse hentlech!
Ch'vel nit fregn dich funvanen—
Ch'vel nit oplozn fundanen.

Ch'vel dich haldzn, ch'vel dich libn.
Iz der bocher dort farblibn.

Oyfn oyvn zitsn tsveyen—
Nit zey heftn, nit zey neyen.

On the oven, there sits a maiden
Embroidering a satin gown.
Came a wild lad running by,
Pulled the thread out on the fly!

Ah you wild lad, ah you lad!
You will wish you never had.

This will cost you very dear
I won't let you out of here!
I won't tie you here with rope,
But within my white hand's scope.

I'll embrace you tenderly,
And you will stay on here, with me.

Now on the oven—two are sitting—
Neither embroidering nor knitting.

NOTE. The last two lines of text are sung to the first two lines of the music.

63

Tsvey Taybelech

This old love song, popularized by Lyuba Levitsky, well-known opera and radio star of Vilna, acquired a special significance in the Vilna ghetto during the Second World War.

For a time under the Nazi occupation, Lyuba managed to hide with Gentile friends beyond the ghetto walls. But when raids were made throughout the city and the suburbs, she returned to the ghetto. Simultaneous with the formation of Partisan brigades in 1942, the cultural life in the ghetto took on new vitality. Lyuba participated actively, singing folk songs and teaching music. The first concert took place on the night following a mass raid and slaughter of some 1500 Jews. The asphalt was still stained with blood. The hall was charged with dread and despair. Fear of sudden encirclement and capture oppressed everyone. That night Lyuba sang *Tsvey taybelech*.

A year later she was scrubbing barracks for the Germans. During one mass round-up she hid for a week in garbage barrels. Another time she was caught and tortured by a Gestapo official, who stamped on her with his boots and pricked her body with the point of his sword. When she recovered she resumed her work in the ghetto, singing for those condemned to death. In an attempt to smuggle through some cooked peas for her sick mother, she was caught, imprisoned, and a month later dragged out to be executed.

She was ordered to undress and walk naked to her death. Lyuba Levitsky walked erect, head high, singing *Tsvey taybelech*, the song that the Jews of the Vilna ghetto will always remember together with the heroic Lyuba.

1 Tsvey taybelech zenen ibern vaser gefloygn
In di piskelech hobn zey zich gekusht.
Farsholtn zol vern yener mentsh
Vos hot zich in undzer libe oy, arayngemisht.

2 Un az du vest kumen in a fremder shtot,
    lyubelyu,
Mayne reyd zolstu badenken!
Un az du vest kumen iber a tifn vaser, lubelyu,
Far groys tsores zolstu zich nisht dertrenken.

3 Un az du vest kumen in a vayter shtot,
    lyubelyu,
Mayne reyd zolstu bakenen!
Un az du vest kumen iber a fayer, lyubelyu,
Far groys tsores zolstu zich nisht farbrenen.

4 Tsvey taybelech zenen ibern vaser gefloygn
Zeyere fligelech hobn zey tsushpreyt.
Kayn gutn sof zol der mentsh nisht hobn
Vos hot undz fun der libe azoy gich tsesheyt!

1 There were two doves flew over the water,
Their bills met kissing high above,
Cursed be that wicked man
Who came between our love!

2 And when you come to a strange town, my dear,
Remember my words tomorrow;
And when you come to a deep water, my own,
Do not drown yourself for sorrow.

3   And when you come to a distant town, my love,
Remember my words tomorrow;
And when you pass a fire, my dear,
Don't burn yourself for sorrow.

4   There were two doves flew over the water
They spread their wings up high above,
No good befall that wicked man
Who tore us from our love!

Genzelech

Dort baym tay-chl, nit vayt fun dem shte-tl,

Pa-shet di gen-ze-lech, a mey-de-le gor sheyn. Di

oyg-lech glan-tsn, oyf li-pe-lech a shmey-chl,

66

1 Dort baym taychl, nit vayt fun dem shtetl,
Pashet di genzelech, a meydele gor sheyn.
Di oyglech glantsn, oyf lipelech a shmeychl,
Zingt zi a lidl oyf aheymtsugeyn:

Chorus:

Hay-la, hay-la, hay-la, hay-la,
loyft-zhe genzelech, aheym, aheym, aheym!

2 Der alter goner, er meg afile platsn!
Vel ich im nit nemen, neyn un neyn un neyn!
Vos toygn mir zayne rayche palatsn?
Ven ich bin noch azoy yung un sheyn?

Chorus

1 On the banks of the river, near by the village,
A pretty maiden is tending her geese.
Her merry eyes sparkle, her soft lips are smiling
As she sings this coming-home song:

Hay-la, hay-la, hay-la, hay-la,
Come along little geese, come home!

2 The old gander can burst if he wants to—
But I won't have him, never, oh no!
What good to me are all of his castles?
While I'm still so pretty and young?

Fishelech Koyfn

Bin ich mir ge - gan - gen fi - she - lech koy - fn Hob ich mir ge -

koyft ___ a hecht. ___ Un ver es iz shul - dig in und - zer

1 Bin ich mir gegangen fishelech koyfn
Hob ich mir gekoyft a hecht.
Un ver es iz shuldig in undzer libe,
Der zol oysgeyen vi a lecht!

Chorus:
    Day, day, day, day, day-day . . .

2 On kayn shteyner, on kayn tsigl
Kon men kayn hoyz nit moyern.
S'iz nisht faranen kayn mentsh oyf der velt
Vos zol mich nisht badoyeren!

Chorus

1 I went to market to buy fish
And I bought a kite.
May he who is guilty of our love
Burn out like a candle light!

2 Without plaster, without bricks,
You cannot build a masonry.
Oh there's no one in all the world
Who does not pity me!

Shpilt–zhe Mir Dem Nayem Sher*

Not too fast

Shpilt - zhe mir dem nay - em___ Sher Vos iz a - roys - ge - ku - nem

Ch'ob zich far - libt in a yin - ge - le a shey - nem Un

kon tsu im nisht ku - men. Ch'volt tsu im ge - ku - men,

Melody

Sher: a form of square dance with partners.

1 Shpilt-zhe mir dem nayem Sher
Vos iz aroysgekumen.
Ch'ob zich farlibt in a yingele a sheynem
Un kon tsu im nisht kumen.
Ch'volt tsu im gekumen,
Voynt er zeyer vayt.
Ch'volt doch im a kush gegebn,
Shem ich zich far layt . . .
Nisht azoy far layt,
Vi far Got aleyn—
Ch'volt mit im farbracht di tsayt
Az keyner zol nisht zeyn.

2 Shpilt-zhe mir dem nayem Sher
Vos iz aroysgekumen.
Ich hob zich farlibt in a yingele a sheynem
Un kon tsu im nisht kumen.
Kum-zhe tsu mir gicher,
Ich vart oyf dir shoyn lang.
Kum shoyn gich ariber,
Men zol nisht hern dayn gang.
Fir ich dich in shtibele
Fun mayn mamen aleyn.
Chosn-kale veln mir zayn
Un tsu der chupe geyn!

1 Play, play the latest tune,
Dance the latest "Sher"—
I have fallen in love with a handsome lad,
But I dare not stir.
I should like to go to him,
But he lives far away.
I should like to kiss him,
But what would people say?
It's not so much what people'd say,
As it is morality—
I should like to be with him,
Where no one else could see.

2 Play, play the latest tune,
Dance the latest "Sher"—
I have fallen in love with a handsome lad,
But I dare not stir.
Oh come to me, come quickly,
I've been waiting long.
Come quietly—but quickly,
So no one may think it wrong.
I'll take you to my mother's hut
Into her very room.
We'll stand under the canopy
And be bride and groom!

Indroysn Iz A Triber Tog

in a fin - ster - er chma - re. Ch'ob chma - re.

1 Indroysn iz a triber tog
In shtibele iz a pa-re;
Ch'ob opgelebt mayne yunge yorn
Vi in a finsterer chmare.

2 Vi in a finsterer chmare
Iz der tog fun mayn geboyrn;
Ich hob gehat a tayern diment
Un hob im ongevoyrn.

3 Ich hob im ongevoyrn,
Un kon im nisht gefinen;
Shteyen shteyt er far mayne oygn
Un ich kon tsu im nisht kimen.

4 Ich kon tsu im nisht kimen,
Ich kon mit im nisht reydn;
Oy, fun undzer heyser libe,
Muzn mir zich tsesheydn.

5 Ale vaserlech loyfn avek,
Di gribelech blaybn leydik;
Oy vu nemt men aza mentshn
Vos zol farshteyn mayn veytik?

6 Azoy vi es iz nishto kayn mentsh
Vos zol konen di shtern ibertseyln,
Azoy iz nishto kayn mentsh
Vos zol konen mayne vunden heyln.

1 'Tis miserable out of doors,
Inside, the hut is steaming;
I have spent all my young life
In a hopeless dreaming.

2 In hopeless dreaming
The day that I was born;
I had a diamond rare
And now it is gone.

3 And now it is gone,
I'll find it nevermore;
There he stands before my eyes,
But on the yonder shore.

4 Upon the yonder shore,
Far from my yearning heart,
I cannot speak with you,
My darling—we must part.

5 All waters flow away,
The wells are dry and hollow;
Oh, where is there the man,
To understand my sorrow?

6 As there is no man
Who can count the stars,
So there is no man
To heal my wounded heart.

73

Vi Azoy Kon Ich Lustig Zayn?

1   Vi azoy kon ich lustig zayn?
Az farshtert zenen mir mayne vegn.
Az ich dermon zich in zayn sheyn ponim,
Vi azoy kon ich lebn?

2   Ich es un trink
Un shlof baynacht.
Nor mayn harts
Iz mir fartracht.

3 *Same as first verse*

1   Then how can I merry be,
Now my love is gone.
Remembering his lovely face,
How can I live on?

2   I eat and drink and sleep
Night and day.
But my heart
Is far, far away.

SONGS OF LIFE AND WORK

SEVERAL hundred years before the rise of the great Jewish center of Eastern Europe, a type of Jewish secular folk song was current among the Jewish communities in Western and Central Europe. About the beginning of the nineteenth century, however, it seemed to fade away, while in the Slavic countries it blossomed forth and continued to thrive right up to the catastrophic years of the Second World War.

Together with the ancient cradle and children's songs, and the later love songs (of the latter half of the nineteenth century), the people sang of their poverty, of their crafts, of their hard work, and expressed themselves with the characteristic simplicity and force of folk art.

The songs of poverty and work reflect a period of development that saw the individual journeyman replaced by the laboring masses of the factories —a passage, musically, from solo to group songs. The wedding songs, which celebrate the high point in the life of the Jewish community, sing along gaily but with an undertone of sadness. Even the gay *Hecher, beser,* or as it is commonly known, *Di Mezinke oysgegebn,* seems to heave a sigh of relief now that the youngest is married off! The nonsense songs laugh at poverty, but there is a wryness to their fun. This is illustrated in *Di geneyve,* which satirizes the "haul" of a burglar whose ill luck it was to choose the poverty-stricken home of the town rabbi.

The hasidic song, with or without words, occupies an important place in Eastern European song. Some of the hasidic rabbis, like the Puritan fathers of colonial America, sought to "rescue a tune" for use in the service of the Lord. They did not hesitate to borrow freely from the tunes of shepherds, the march rhythms of passing regiments, the songs of the peasants in the fields. The notion that while the life of a text is limited the melody lives on forever, resulted in a preponderance of songs without words. Each composer of a hasidic melody created according to his own particular mood and temperament, in an effort to achieve the closest possible communion with the Creator. These tunes, chants and dances were then carried into every corner of Eastern Europe by the followers [Hasidim] of the various rabbis' courts.

The airs were in turn refashioned by the people, and resulted in a great many variants on individual tunes.

In the period of decline of the hasidic movement, during the last quarter of the nineteenth century, a number of anti-hasidic songs were current among the people. Many of these were composed by Mitnagdim, Maskilim, and others opposed to hasidism. Such songs derided the allegedly bureaucratic rule of the rabbis, pointing up their wealth as contrasted with the deep poverty, backwardness and ignorance of their disciples. Musically, hasidic song left a strong imprint on Eastern European Jewish music as a whole. Very little, however, has been done to gather together this remarkable collection of song.

Zuntig — Bulbe

2 Broyt mit bulbe,
Fleysh mit bulbe,
Varimes un vetshere—bulbe.
Ober un vider—bulbe.
Eynmol in a novine—a bulbe kigele!
Zuntig vayter bulbe.

3 Ober—bulbe,
Vider—bulbe,
Noch amol un ober amol—bulbe!
Haynt un morgn—bulbe!
Ober Shabes nochn tsholnt—a bulbe kigele!
Zuntig—vayter bulbe.

1 Sunday—'taters,
Monday—'taters,
Tuesday and Wednesday—'taters,
Thursday and Friday—'taters,
Sabbath, for a special treat—there's a 'tater pudding!
Sunday—starts with 'taters.

2 Bread and 'taters,
Meat and 'taters,
Lunch and dinner—'taters.
Over and over—'taters.
Once for a special treat—there's a 'tater pudding!
Sunday—starts with 'taters.

3 Still—'taters,
Ever—'taters,
Always, always, always 'taters!
Today and tomorrow—'taters!
After Sabbath pot roasts—there's a 'tater pudding!
Sunday—starts with 'taters.

Mit A Nodl, On A Nodl

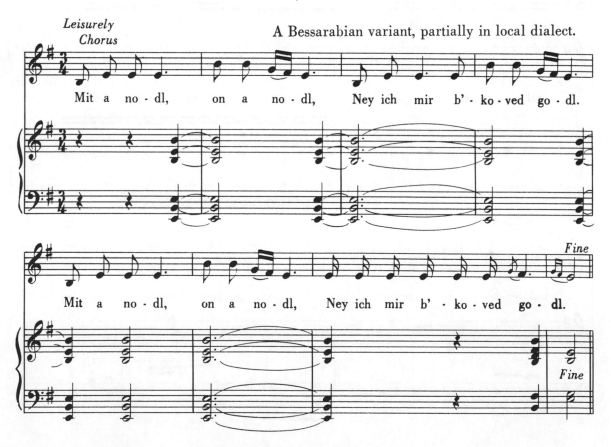

Leisurely
Chorus

A Bessarabian variant, partially in local dialect.

Mit a no-dl, on a no-dl, Ney ich mir b'-ko-ved go-dl.

Mit a no-dl, on a no-dl, Ney ich mir b'-ko-ved go-dl.

Fine

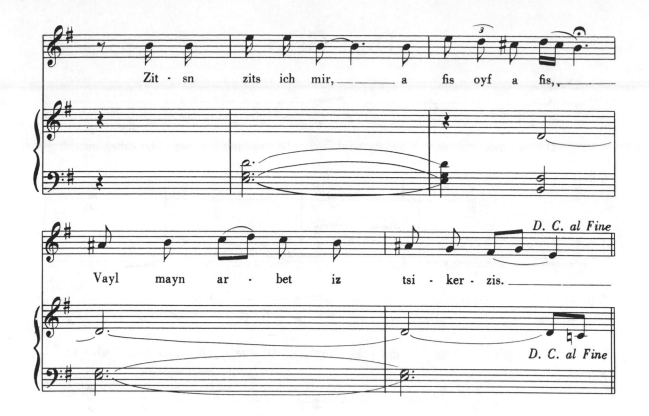

D. C. al Fine

Chorus:

Mit a nodle, on a nodl,
Ney ich mir b'koved godl.

1 Zitsn zits ich mir, a fis oyf a fis,
Vayl mayn arbet iz tsiker-zis.

   Chorus

2 Ich ney un ney, a gantse voch,
Un ney mir oys a Parizer loch.

   Chorus

3 Tsi-en, tsi ich mir di fastrige.
Un ich es mir di mamelige.

   Chorus

4 Shabes gey ich aroys, vi ın posik shteyt,
In di eygene b'godim vos ich hob aleyn geneyt!

   Chorus

With a needle or without a needle,
Here I sit, proud as a beadle.

1 Here I sit and cross my feet,
Because my work is sugar-sweet.

2 I sew and sew the whole week through,
My work's as good as Paris, too.

3 I pull out the basting thread,
And enjoy my sweet cornbread.

4 Sabbath, I turn up à la mode,
In the suit my hands have sewed!

Dire-Gelt

Di - re - gelt un oy - oy - oy!____ Di - re - gelt un bo - zhe - moy!

Di - re - gelt un gra - do - voy!____ Di - re - gelt muz men tso - ln.

Kumt a - rayn der struzh,____ Nemt er a - rop dos hi - tl. Un

az men tsolt kayn di - re - gelt____ Hengt er a - roys a kvi - tl.

Chorus:

Dire-gelt un oy-oy-oy!
Dire gelt un bozhemoy!
Dire-gelt un gradovoy!
Dire-gelt muz men tsoln.

1 Kumt arayn der struzh,
Nemt er arop dos hitl.
Un az men tsolt kayn dire-gelt
Hengt er aroys a kvitl.

   Chorus

2 Kumt arayn der balabos,
Mit dem grobn shtekn,
Un az men git nit kayn dire-gelt,
Shtelt er aroys di betn.

   Chorus

3 Farvos zol ich tsoln dire-gelt
Az di kich iz tsebrochn?
Farvos zol ich gebn dire-gelt
Az ich hob nisht oyf vos tsu kochn?

   Chorus

NOTE. Observe the musical pattern of this song; the chorus is sung one way preceding each verse, and differently following each verse.

Rent to pay, oh my, oh my,
Rent to pay, O God on high.
Rent to pay, the cop's near by!
You'd better pay your rent!

1 First the "super" comes,
He's respectful yet.
But if your rent's not paid—
Your apartment's "to let".

2 Then the landlord comes,
Swinging his thick cane.
And if you don't pay your rent-
You are out in the rain.

3 But why should I pay rent
When my stove's in such a state?
And why should I pay rent
When I can't cook on the grate?

Lomir Ale Zingen—A Zemerl

Lo - mir a - le zin - gen, Lo - mir a - le zin - gen, A

ze - mer - l, a ze - mer - l, Le - chem iz broyt,____

bo - ser v' do - gim, V' chol ma - ta - a - mim.

Zog - zhe mir ta - te - nyu, vos____ iz le - chem? Bay di

groy - se n' - gi - dim, iz le - chem a vay - sin - ke bul - ke - le. O - ber bay

undz kab - tso - nim, oy, dal - fo - nim, Iz

le - chem a da - re sko - rin - ke.

D. C. al Fine

Chorus:

Lomir ale zingen, lomir ale zingen,
A zemerl, a zemerl,
Lechem iz broyt, boser v'dogim,
V'chol mata-amim.

1 Zog-zhe mir tatenyu, vos iz lechem?
Bay di groyse n'gidim, iz lechem a vaysinke
      bulkele.
Ober bay undz kabtsonim, oy, dalfonim,
Iz lechem a dare skorinke.

   Chorus

Chorus:

Let's all sing together, let's all sing together,
A jolly tune, a jolly tune.
Lechem is bread, *boser v'dogim,*
V'chol mat'amim.

1 Tell me, daddy, what does *lechem* mean?
--To a rich man, *lechem* means a white roll.
But to us poor folk, oh, down-and-out folk,
Lechem is a dry crust of bread.

85

2 Zog-zhe mir tatenyu, vos iz boser?
Bay di groyse n'gidim, iz boser a gebrotene
   katshkele.
Ober bay undz kabtsonim, oy, dalfonim,
Iz boser an ayngedarte kishkele.

   Chorus

2 Tell me, daddy, what does *boser* mean?
—To a rich man, *boser* means roast duck.
But to us poor folk, oh, down-and-out folk,
Boser is a shriveled piece of neck-meat.

3 Zog-zhe mir tatenyu, vos iz dogim?
Bay di groyse n'gidim, iz dogim a frish-tsapldig
   hechtele.
Ober bay undz kabtsonim, oy, dalfonim
Iz dogim an oysgeveykter heringl.

   Chorus

3 Tell me, daddy, what does *dogim* mean?
—To a rich man, *dogim* means a fresh pike.
But to us poor folk, oh, down-and-out folk,
Dogim is a tasteless herring.

4 Zog-zhe mir tatenyu, vos iz mata-amim?
Bay di groyse n'gidim, iz mata-amim a geshmaker
   tsimes.
Ober bay undz kabtsonim, oy, dalfonim,
Iz mata-amim—gehakte tsores!

   Chorus

4 Tell me, daddy, what does *mat'amim* mean?
—To a rich man, *mat'amim* means delicious compote.
But to us poor folk, oh, down-and-out folk,
Mat'amim is just a mess of trouble!

Ot Azoy Neyt A Shnayder

This well-known work song began its travels about the middle of the 19th century. The first two verses belong to the period of the independent handicraftsmen. The third was born in the eighties, during the struggle for the ten-hour day. The fourth seems to indicate a successful strike.

86

Chorus:
Ot azoy neyt a shnayder,
Ot azoy neyt er doch!

This is the way a tailor sews.
This is how he really sews!

1   Er neyt un neyt a gantse voch,
Fardint a gildn mit a loch!
Chorus

1   He sews and sews the whole week long,
And earns a penny and a song.

2   A shnayder neyt un neyt un neyt,
Un hot kadoches, nit kayn broyt!
Chorus

2   A tailor sews to earn his bread,
But gets the misery, instead.

3   Farayorn, nit haynt-gedacht!
Hobn mir gehorevet fun acht biz acht!
Chorus

3   A year ago, we all worked late,
(Never again!)—from eight to eight!

4   Ober di struktsie hot ongemacht,
Mir arbetn shoyn mer nit fun acht biz acht!
Chorus

4   But the "union" set us straight,
We work no more from eight to eight!

Indroysn Geyt A Drobinker Regn

Poignant

In - droy - sn geyt __ a dro - bin - ker re - gn, Ay, di vol - ken - es, zey

ho - bn zich far - shpreyt. __ Tsayt ich hob __ nor di be - ke - ray der -

kent, __ A - zoy hot zich mir der kop __ far - dreyt. __

1 Indroysn geyt a drobinker regn,
Ay, di volkenes, zey hobn zich farshpreyt.
Tsayt ich hob nor di bekeray derkent,
Azoy hot zich mir der kop fardreyt.

2 A mil az zi molt, molt zi keseyder,
Far ir opshtel iz oych do a minut.
Kukt nor on dos klenste beker-yingl,
Tsi farmogt er den a tropn blut!

3 Der beker mit der bekern, zey kumen in der
       bekeray,
Loyt zeyer raychtum un loyt zeyer shteyger:
Zi geyt ongeton a por brilyantene oyringen,
Un er in a goldenem zeyger.   4 *Same as first verse*

38

1 Outdoors the rain is dropping slow,
Oh, clouds have gathered over me.
My head's been spinning ever since
I first came to this bakery.

2 Though the windmill turn and turn,
There comes a moment of standstill.
But the poor pale baker boy
Never can and never will.

3 The baker and the baker's wife,
Come dressed in all their finery:
She with a pair of brilliants,
With a gold watch comes he!

Zhamele

This satirical poem was written by A. Litwin (Sh. Hurwitz), who died several years ago. He was a journalist who wrote for the American Yiddish press for many years, and also collected Jewish folklore. The composer of the tune is unknown. "Zhamele" is popular in America and is sung to various melodies.

With gentle irony

Du vest zayn a g'vir, mayn Zha - me - le,

Flegt mir zin gen bay mayn vi - ge - le A - le nacht a - mol, mayn

ma - me - le, Ich ge - denk noch haynt ir - ni - ge - le.

1 Du vest zayn a g'vir, mayn Zhamele,
Flegt mir zingen bay mayn vigele
Ale nacht amol, mayn mamele,
Ich gedenk noch haynt ir nigele.

2 Un meku-im iz gevorn mir
Di havtoches fun mayn mamele.
Shver tsu krign aza grosyn g'vir,
Aza'n oysher vi ir Zhamele!

3 Shlofn, shlof ich oyf a kerbele,
Mach hamoytse oyf a skorinke,
Un lechayim oyf a sherbele
Ful mit brunim vaser klorinke.

4 Un di kinderlech, un s'vaybele,
Geyen oysgeputst antikele!
Durch in onitses dos laybele—
Un fargartlt mit a shtrikele!

1 You'll be rich one day, my Zhamele,
Mother used to sing to me.
Every evening at my cradle,
Still I hear that melody.

2 Now my mother's fondest dreams
Have become reality.
There is not another one,
As rich as Zhamele, her son!

3 I sleep—on a bed of straw,
Thank the Lord for a crust of bread,
Broken shards—my toasting cup,
I sip fresh water—from the well.

4 And my darling wife and children,
Dress up quite in latest style!
Wearing shirts of rags and tatters
Held up with a hempen rope!

Laytishe Mazoles

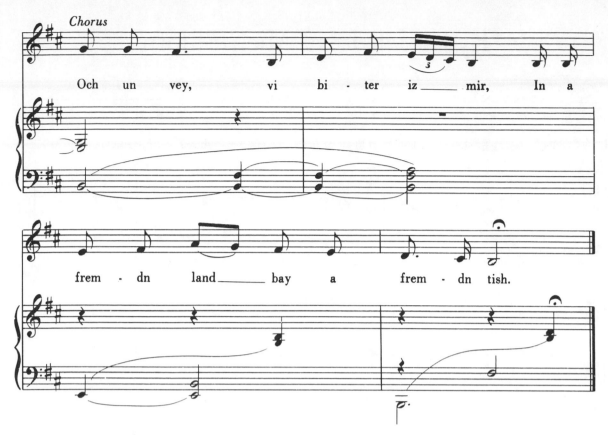

Och un vey, vi bi-ter iz ___ mir, In a frem-dn land ___ bay a frem-dn tish.

1 Laytishe mazoles tu-en oyfn vaser shvimen,
Ich zuch mayn mazl un kon nit gefinen.

Chorus:

Och un vey, vi biter iz mir,
In a fremdn land bay a fremdn tish.

2 Mayn baleboste zogt: es! nit shem zich!
Un in hartsn tracht zi: tsum broyt nit zem zich!

Chorus

3 Mayn mame fleg mir gebn esn un zogn: es,
mayn kind,
In hartsn fleg zi trachtn: zayn zolstu gezunt.

Chorus

4 Un az mayn mame zol dos visn,
Az ich shlof baynacht gor on a kishn.

Chorus

5 Bay mayn mamen bin ich geven choshev un
tayer,
Vi bay an oriman, an eyntsiger drayer.

Chorus

1 I keep seeking my fortune, but it passes me by,
Other people seem to find it, but not I.

Chorus:

Alack and alas, oh woe is me!
To be far from home and eat the bread of poverty!

2 My landlady says: Now, don't be bashful, eat!
But in her heart she thinks: Go easy on the meat!

3 My mother used to say: Eat, my darling son,
And in her heart she thought: Grow strong, my precious
one.

4 If mother only saw, the board I call my bed,
And that I sleep at night without a pillow to my head!

5 Like the apple of her eye, my mother treasured me,
As a poor man guards his last precious penny.

Eyder Ich Leyg Mich Shlofn

With pathos

Ey - der ich leyg mich shlo - fn, Darf ich shoyn oyf - shteyn. Mit

may - ne kran - ke bey - ner Tsu der ar - bet geyn.

Chorus

Tsu Got vel ich vey - nen, ___ Mit a groys ge - veyn! Tsu

vos ich bin ge - boy - rn A ney - tor - in tsu zayn!

1   Eyder ich leyg mich shlofn,
Darf ich shoyn oyfshteyn.
Mit mayne kranke beyner
Tsu der arbet geyn.

Chorus:

Tsu Got vel ich veynen,
Mit a groys geveyn!
Tsu vos ich bin geboyrn
A neytorin tsu zayn!

2   Ich kum shpet tsu der arbet,
S'iz doch vayt der veg—
Shlogt men mir op
Far halbe teg!

Chorus

3   Nodlen vern tsubrochn,
Fuftsn a minut.
Di finger vern tsushtochn,
Es rint fun zey dos blut.

Chorus

4   Ich layd shtendig hunger,
Ich hob nisht vos tsu esn.
Vil ich gelt betn,
Heyst men mir fargesn!

Chorus

1   No sooner in my bed
Then I must up again.
To drag my weary limbs
Off to work again.

To God I will cry,
With a great outcry!
Why was I born
To be a seamstress, why?

2   Should I once come late,
'Tis a long way—
They dock me straight off
A full half-day!

3   The machines are old,
The needles they break.
My bleeding fingers—
Oh, how they ache!

4   I've nothing to eat,
I'm hungry all the day.
They tell me: forget it!
When I ask for pay!

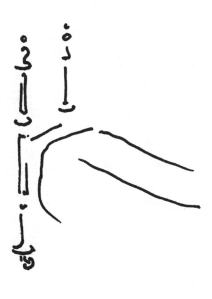

Az Men Fort Kayn Sevastopol

Az men fort kayn Se - vas - to - pol, Iz nit vayt fun Sim - fer - o - pol,

Dor - tn iz a stan - tsi - e far - an. Ver darf zu - chn

nay - e gli - kn? S'iz a stan - tsie an an - ti - kl, In Zhan - ko - ye,

zhan, zhan, zhan. Hey zhan, hey Zhan - ko - ye,

2 Entfert Yidn oyf mayn kashe,
Vu'z mayn bruder, vu'z Abrasha?
S'geyt bay im der trakter vi a ban.
Di mume Leye bay der kosilke,
Beyle bay der molotilke,
In Zhankoye, zhan, zhan, zhan.

Chorus

3 Ver zogt as Yidn konen nor handlen
Esn fete yoych mit mandlen,
Nor nit zayn kayn arbetsman?
Dos konen zogn nor di sonim!
Yidn! Shpayt zey on in ponim!
Tut a kuk oyf zhan, zhan, zhan!

Chorus

1 On the road to Sevastopol,
Not too far from Simferopol,
There's a railroad station.
Why go looking high and low?
There's no finer station, no!
Than Zhankoye, zhan, zhan, zhan.

2 Tell me brothers, if you can,
Where's Abrasha? Where's that man?
His tractor's racing like a fan.
Aunt Leye is at the reaper,
And Beyle is at the thresher,
In Zhankoye, zhan, zhan, zhan.

3 Who says Jews can only trade,
Eat fat soups and not create,
Nor be sturdy workingmen?
Enemies can talk like that!
Jews! Let's spit right in their eye!
Just you look at zhan, zhan, zhan.

This is a farm song from Jewish settlements in the Crimea of the middle 20's.

95

Tog Azoy Vi Nacht

Tog a - zoy vi nacht____ un nacht a - zoy vi tog, Un

ney - en un ney - en un ney - en! Un ney - en un ney - en un

ney - en! Helf mir shoyn Go - te - nyu, mayn shey - ner zol shoyn ku - men, Un

fun der ar - bet zol ich a - vek gey - en.

2　Noch amol geneyt un vider amol geneyt,
Geneyt un geneyt un geshtochn!
Oy du ziser Gotenyu, du veyst doch dem emes,
Az mayne beyner zenen mir tsubrochn.

3　Tog azoy vi nacht un nacht azoy vi tog,
Un neyen un neyen un neyen!
Got zol mir shoyn helfn, di frayhayt zol shoyn
　　kumen,
Un ich zol zich shoyn gicher, mit ir zeyen!

1　Day the same as night, night the same as day,
And all I do is sew and sew and sew.
May God help me, and my love come soon,
That I may leave this work and go.

2　Sewing and sewing, sewing on and on,
Stitch and hem, and stitch and hem again,
Oh, sweet God, you know the bitter truth,
How my eyes do ache and my fingers pain.

3　Day the same as night, night the same as day,
And all I do is sew and sew and pine.
Oh, God help me, bring freedom soon,
That I may raise my eyes and see it shine!

Nem Aroys A Ber Fun Vald

With a twinkle in your eye

Nem a - roys　a　ber fun vald　Un lern＿ im　oys＿ shray - bn.

De - mlt ves - tu,　de - mlt ves - tu　Ey - big may - ner　blay - bn!

97

SHE: 1 Nem aroys a ber fun vald
Un lern im oys shraybn.
Demlt vestu, demlt vestu
Eybig mayner blaybn!

HE: 2 Ich vel aroysnemen a ber fun vald
Un vel im oyslernen shraybn.
Mach-zhe mir zibn hemder
On nodl un on zaydn.

SHE: 3 Ich vel dir machn zibn hemder
On nodl un on zaydn.
Boy mir oys a leyter hoych,
Tsum himl zol er shtaygn.

HE: 4 Ich vel dir oysboyen a leyter hoych
Tsum himl vet er shtaygn.
Hob-zhe mir zibn kinder,
A meydl zolstu blaybn!

SHE: 5 Ich vel dir hobn zibn kinder
Un a meydl blaybn.
Boy mir oys zibn vign
On holts un on getsaygn.

HE: 6 Ich vel dir oysboyen zibn vign
On holts un on getsaygn.
Bizt doch a kluge, un ich kayn nar—
To lomir beyde blaybn!

1 Lead a bear out of the woods
And teach him how to write.
You'll be mine for evermore
If you are that bright!

2 I'll lead a bear out of the woods
And he will write, you'll see;
But you must use no cloth or thread,
Making seven shirts for me.

3 Oh I will use no cloth or thread
And make your shirts, all seven.
Build me then a ladder tall,
That reaches up to heaven.

4 I shall build you a ladder tall
To reach the sky at will.
Bear me seven children, and
Remain a maiden still.

5 I shall bear you seven children
And still remain a maid.
Make me seven cribs without
Wood or tools to aid.

6 Seven cribs I'll make for you
And use no wood or tool.
Let us put our hearts together,
For you are wise—and I'm no fool!

Kegn Gold Fun Zun

A farm song from Jewish settlements in the Ukraine of the middle 20's.

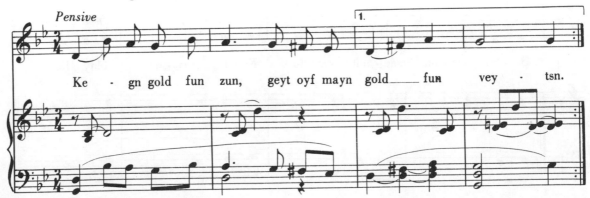

Ke - gn gold fun zun, geyt oyf mayn gold___ fun vey - tsn.

98

1   Kegn gold fun zun, geyt oyf mayn gold fun veytsn.

Kegn gold fun zun, geyt oyf mayn goldn glik.

Naye horizontn rufn mich un reytsn,

Naye lider zing ich, Yidisher muzhik.

2   Geyt di arbet freylech, fun gantsfri biz ovnt,

Zun iz mayn hudok un feld iz mayn fabrik.

Nechtn sh-cheynim vayte, haynt shoyn azoy novnt,

Ukra-iner poyer, Yidisher muzhik.

1   Toward the golden sun springs my golden wheat,

Toward the golden sun springs my golden joy.

Broad horizons beckon, bid me rise and plow,

New songs sing within me, Jewish farmer now.

2   The work goes swift and happy, from sunrise until night,

The sun is my whistle, the field my factory.

Yesterday, far neighbors, comrades near, today,

Ukrainian peasant, you—Jewish farmer, me.

Un Du Akerst Un Du Zeyst

In 1864, Georges Herwegh, following the theme of Shelley's "Song to the Men of England," wrote a hymn for the German Workingmen's Federation. The Yiddish text given here is a translation of Herwegh's poem by Chaim Zhitlowsky.

Tsu-rayst di key - tn fun shkla - fn tsvang!

1 Un du akerst un du zeyst,
Un du fiterst un du neyst,
Un du hamerst un du shpinst,
Zog mayn folk vos du fardinst?

Chorus:

Kling klang, kling klang,
Klapt der hamer mit zayn gezang;
Kling klang, kling klang,
Tsurayst di keytn fun shklafn tsvang.

2 Vebst dayn vebshtul tog un nacht,
Grobst undz ayzn fun der shacht,
Brengst di shefa undz arayn,
Ful mit tvue un mit vayn.

3 Nor vu iz dayn tish gegreyt?
Nor vu iz dayn yomtov kleyd?
Nor vu iz dayn sharfe shverd?
Velches glik iz dir bashert?

1 You are the plowmen and you sow,
You are the farmers and you mow,
And you toil with might and main:
What, my people, is your gain?

Chorus:
Kling klang, kling klang,
The hammer beats relentlessly.
Kling klang, kling klang,
Break the bonds of slavery.

2 Day and night you weave on the loom,
Dig out metals in the gloom,
Reap thè hàrvest in due time,
Flowing horn of bread and wine.

3 But what feasts have you to share?
And what festive clothes to wear?
Where, my people, 's your sharp sword?
Where, oh where is your reward?

101

Gibn Dir Mayn Tochter

Gi - bn dir mayn toch - ter, A shus - ter far a man?

A shus - ter far a man vil ich nit, A shus - ter's a toch - ter

bin ich nit, La - ten shti - vl kon ich nit. Zitz ich oyf a

shteyn, Un kuk a - rop un veyn, Un ze vi a - le

meyd - lech ho - bn cha - se - ne   Un nor   ich blayb a - leyn.

2   Gibn dir mayn tochter,
A shnayder far a man?
A shnayder far a man vil ich nit,
A shnayder's a tochter bin ich nit,
Neyen kleyder kon ich nit.
   Zits ich oyf a shteyn,
   Un kuk arop un veyn,
   Un ze vi ale meydlech hobn chasene
   Un nor ich blayb aleyn.

3   Gibn dir mayn tochter,
A lamdn far a man?
A lamdn far a man vil ich yo!
A lamdn's a tochter bin ich yo!
Toyre lernen kon ich yo!
   Zits ich oyfn dach,
   Un kuk arop un lach!
   Un ze vi ale meydlech hobn chasene
   Un ich bin mit zey glaych!

1   My dear, my darling daughter,
Will you be a cobbler's wife?
The wife of a cobbler I will not be,
The daughter of a cobbler I am not,
Patch old boots—I cannot.
   I sit upon a stone,
   Hang my head and moan:
   All the girls are getting married—
   And I am left alone!

2   My dear, my darling daughter,
Will you be a tailor's wife?
The wife of a tailor I will not be,
The daughter of a tailor I am not,
Stitch and sew—I cannot.
   I sit upon a stone,
   Hang my head and moan:
   All the girls are getting married—
   And I am left alone!

3   My dear, my darling daughter,
Will you be a scholar's wife?
A scholar's wife, yes, that I'll be,
The daughter of a scholar—that I am,
Learn the Torah—that I can!
   Upon the roof sit I,
   Laughing merrily,
   For you have given me my true mate,
   Now, all do envy me!

103

Di Mezinke Oysgegebn

Morris (Mark) Warshavsky (1848-1907), "discovered" by Sholom Aleichem, is author both of text and tune of this song. He was a true folk poet
and composer; most people are unaware even today that he was author and
composer of so many of their beloved songs. Some of these are: *Oyfn pripet-
shek brent a fayerl, Der becher, Dos lid fun broyt, Der zeyde mit der bobe*
(or *Achtsig er un zibetsiz zi*), *Dem milner's trern.*

1 Shtarker, beser!
Di rod, di rod macht greser!
Groys hot mich Got gemacht.
Glik hot er mir gebracht.
Hulyet kinder, a gantse nacht!
Di mezinke oysgegebn!

2 Motl, Shimen—
Di orimelayt zenen gekimen.
Shtelt zey dem shenstn tish,
Tayere vaynen, tayere fish,
Oy vey tochter, gib mir a kish!
Di mezinke oysgegebn!

3 Ayzik, mazik!
Di bobe geyt a kozik!
Kayn ayn-ore, zet nor zet!
Vi zi tupet, vi zi tret!
Oy a simche, oy a freyd!
Di mezinke oysgegebn!

4 Itzik, shpitzik—
Vos shvaygstu mit dem shmitshik?
Oyf di klezmer tu a geshrey!
Tsi shpiln zey, tsi shlofn zey?
Rayst di strunes ale oyf tsvey!
Di mezinke oysgegebn!

1 Larger, longer,
Make the dance-ring stronger!
God has brought me great delight,
Made my dark days sunny, bright,
So dance, my children, with all your might!
I've given my youngest away tonight!

2 Motl, Shimen—
All the poor folk have arrived.
Serve them the best of every dish,
Costly wines, delicious fish,
Oh my daughter, give me a kiss!
I've given my youngest away tonight!

3 Isaac, you rascal,
We're in for a treat!
Just you watch Granny
How she stamps her feet!
What joy, oh what delight!
I've given my youngest away tonight!

4 Itzik, old fellow,
Raise your bow—and bellow
At your band, that lazy crew,
Strike up the liveliest of tunes!
Until you burst your strings in two!
I've given my youngest away tonight!

Chatskele, Chatskele

A poor uninvited aunt asks the fiddler (Chatskele) to play her tunes to dance to (*kazatske, dume, semele*). She is poor but proud, and full of spirit, and brings her humble *drayerl* (three-kopek piece) to help the young bride establish herself in a stall (*kremele*) at the market place, so that her husband may pursue his studies of the Torah.

Lo - mir zich nit she - men mit ey - ge - nem blut!

1   Chatskele, Chatskele, shpil mir a kazatskele,
Chotsh an orime, abi a chvatske!

Chorus:

  Orim iz nit gut, orim iz nit gut,
  Lomir zich nit shemen mit eygenem blut!

2   Chatskele, Chatskele, shpil mir a dume,
Un chotsh an orime, abi a frume!

  Chorus

3   Nit kayn gebetene, aleyn gekumen!
Chotsh an orimenke, fort a mume!

  Chorus

4   Chatskele, Chatskele, shpil-zhe mir a semele,
Far a drayerl oyf Chaske's kremele.

  Chorus

1   Chatskele, Chatskele, play me a kazatske,
Though she be poor, yet she has spirit!

  Poverty's no good, poverty's no good,
  Let's not be ashamed of our own flesh and blood.

2   Chatskele, Chatskele, play me a dume,
Though she be poor, yet she is pious!

3   She wasn't invited, but came to the wedding,
Though she be poor, an aunt's still an aunt!

4   Chatskele, Chatskele, play me a semele,
And accept my humble gift for the bride so sweet.

Oyfn Barg, Ibern Barg

1 Oyfn bar, ibern barg,
Fli-en toybn porn.
Noch gor kayn naches nit derlebt
Avek mayne yunge yorn.

2 Shpant-zhe brider, ferd un vogn,
Lomir loyfn, yogn!
Tomir veln mir noch deryogn
Undzere yunge yorn.

3 Shoyn deryogt di yunge yorn
Oyf der hoycher brik;
Yorn, yorn, kert zich um,
Chotsh in gest tsurik.

4 Neyn, neyn, mirn zich nit umkern—
S'iz nito tsu vemen;
Hot ir fri-er nit gedarft
Undz azoy farshemen!

1 Over the hill, beyond the hill,
Doves in pairs do fly.
I have had no pleasure from
My youth that has flown by.

2 Harness, brothers, horse to wagon,
Let us gallop ahead!
Perhaps we may yet overtake
Our youth that has fled.

3 We did overtake our youth
At the drawbridge gate;
Youth, youth, turn back again,
If only for a space.

4 No, no, we can't turn back,
There's no one to turn for;
You ought not to have
Shamed us so before!

S'hot Gelebt Mit Undz A Chaver

(*The refrain "ay-ay, ay-ay, ay!" is sung after each line of the text.*)

2 Fun der shtot aropgekumen
Hot er undz tsunoyfgenumen.

3 Hodi, kukn oyf di shtern
A kolvirt zol bay undz vern!

4 Lomir trinken a lechayim!
Far dem lebn far dem nayim!

5 Far di felder, far di zate
Far der nayer hoycher chate!

6 Lomir trinker a lechayim!
Far di kinder, far di traye!

7 Far di kinder, far di z'keynim!
Un far alemen ineynim!

1 Once, living in our midst we had
A comrade, a fine sturdy lad.

2 He came from town to be with us
To make us all unanimous.

3 Stop your gazing at the sky!
Collectivize now, not by and by!

4 So let's all drink a toast in wine
To the new and happy time.

5 Toast the rich and fertile ground
Toast the new farm we shall found.

6 So let's all toast once more
Our own children, true and dear.

7 Toast the young and toast the old,
Toast ourselves both young and old!

In Der Kuznye

Morris Rosenfeld, author of this poem, was one of four outstanding Yiddish labor poets in America during the eighties and nineties of the past century. The other three were Morris Winchevsky, David Edelstadt and I. Bovshover. Their poems achieved such widespread popularity that many were set to music, often by composers unknown to us, and were sung among the people both here and abroad. Some of the songs, especially several by David Edelstadt, took such firm root that they are still circulating among Yiddish-speaking workingmen and women on both sides of the Atlantic. This particular song is still current here, in several musical variants.

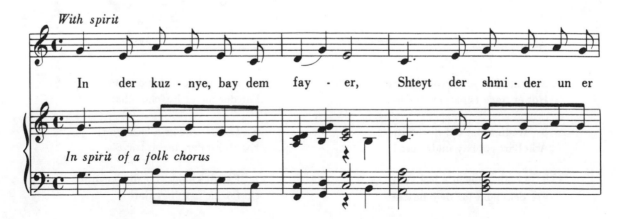

1 In der kuznye bay dem fayer
Shteyt der shmider un er shmit.
Er klapt dos ayzn funken fayer flien,
Un er zingt derbay a lid.

2 Fun der frayhayt vos vet kumen,
Zingt er mutig zingt er heys;
Un er shpirt nit vi es gist zich
Fun zayn ponim taychn shveys.

3 Shtark batsoybert fun der frayhayt,
Zingt er vayter un es klingt;
Nor der hamer klapt noch hecher
Un er hert nit vos er zingt.

4 Un di erd batsirt mit blumen,
Zingt er vayter in zayn lid;
Opgekilt iz shoyn dos ayzn
Un er klapt un vert nit mid.

1 In the smithy at the fire
Stands the blacksmith stout and strong.
Sparks fly as he strikes the iron;
As he strikes, he sings a song.

2 Heartily and bold he sings of
Freedom that will come apace.
And he does not feel as streams of
Sweat go pouring down his face.

3 All enraptured by this freedom,
He bursts into joyous shout.
But his hammer rings still louder,
And his song is blotted out.

4 "Let the earth be strewn with flowers"—
His song is of a better day.
Long ago the iron's cooled,
But he tireless pounds away.

Mechuteneste Mayne

Me - chu - te - nes - te may - ne, me - chu - ten - es - te ge -

tray - e, Lo - mir zayn oyf ey - big me - chu - to -

nim. Lo - mir zayn oyf ey - big me - chu - to - nim.

Ich gib aych a - vek mayn toch - ter far a shnur, Zi

zol bay aych nit on - ver - n dos po - nim.

1 Mechuteneste mayne, mechuteneste getraye,
Lomir zayn oyf eybig mechutonim.
Ich gib aych avek mayn tochter far a shnur,
Zi zol bay aych nit onvern dos ponim.

2 Mechuteneste mayne, mechuteneste getraye,
Mayn kind zolt ir fri nit vekn.
Un tomir vet ir zen an avle oyf mayn kind,
Vi an eygene mame zolt ir dos fardekn.

3 Mechuteneste mayne, mechuteneste getraye,
Oyf kinder hobn tut men blut fargisn.
Un tomir vet ir zen az der zun hot lib di shnur,
Zol es aych gornit fardrisn.

4 Mechuteneste mayne, mechuteneste getraye,
Ich for tsu aych in a parikl.
Nor tomir vet ir zayn a shlak, a beyze shviger,
Iz mayn tochter oych a shnurl—an antikl!

1 Dear relation, sweet relation,
Oh let us always be good relations!
I give you my daughter for to be your daughter-in-law,
May you cause her no humiliation.

2 Dear relation, sweet relation,
Don't wake my child up early with the sun.
And if my child displeases you in any way,
Why, just you overlook it, as I would have done.

3 Dear relation, sweet relation,
There's a lot of blood lost when a child is born,
And should you see your son loves your daughter-in-law,
Don't take it so to heart and do not mourn!

4 Dear relation, sweet relation,
Wearing my wig, I come to visit you.
But if you prove to be a nasty mother-in-law,
Why then, my daughter too, can be a shrew!

Di Gilderne Pave

Es iz ge - floy - gn, di gil - der - ne pa - ve, I - ber a - le___ ya - men.

Loz ge - ri - sn, du gil - der - ner foy - gl, Mayn li - ber, har - tsi - ger ma - men. Loz ge - ri - sn, du gil - der - ne foy - gl, Mayn li - ber, har - tsi - ger ma - men.

1 Es iz gefloygn, di gilderne pave,
Iber ale yamen.
Loz gerisn, du gilderner foygl,
Mayn liber, hartsiger mamen.

2 Gefloygn, gefloygn, di gilderne pave,
Ibern taych dem glatn—
Los gerisn, du gilderner foygl,
Mayn libn, hartsign tatn.

3 Gefloygn, gefloygn, di gilderne pave,
Iber ale felder.
Hot zi farloyrn dem gildernem feder,
In di fremde lender.

4 Nit azoy di gilderne feder,
Vi di pave aleyn.
Nit azoy der fremder zun,
Vi di tochter aleyn.

5 Vi es iz biter, mayn libe muter,
A vaser on a fish,
Azoy iz biter, mayn libe muter,
Bay a fremdn tish.

6 Vi es iz biter, mayn libe muter,
A feygele on a nest,
Azoy iz biter, mayn libe muter
Shver un shviger's kest.

1 The golden peacock came a-flying,
Over land and water.
Bring greetings, O golden bird,
To my darling mother.

2 The golden peacock came a-flying,
Over the smooth, clear sea.
Bring greetings, O golden bird,
To my dear father from me.

3 The golden peacock came a-flying,
Over field and heather,
In a far-off land she lost
Her lovely, golden feather.

4 It is not so much the golden feather,
As the peacock, mother dear,
It is not so much the new-found son,
As your daughter, mother dear.

5 Bitter as it is, dear mother,
For a lake to have no fish,
So is it bitter, dear mother,
To eat from a stranger's dish.

6 Bitter as it is, dear mother,
For a bird to have no nest,
So is it bitter, dear mother,
To be your in-law's unwelcome guest.

Bayt–zhe Mir Oys A Finf–un–tsvantsiger

Bayt - zhe mir oys a finf - un - tsvan - tsi - ger, Oyf

sam - e - rod - no dray - er. Un shpilt - zhe mir klez -

mo - rim - lech, A li - de - le a tay - er.

Chorus

Rom - tshe - rim - tshi, rom - tshe - rim - tshi, Rom - tshe - rim - tshi,

116

rom - tshe - ra. Rom - tshe - rim - tshi, rom - tshe - rim - tshi,

Rom - tshe - rim tshi, rom - tshe - ra

A wedding guest keeps tipping the bandsmen till his legs can no **longer move** so fast.

2 Bayt-zhe mir oys a finf-un-tsvantsiger,
Oyf samerodno firer,
Un shpilt-zhe mir klezmorimlech,
Dos zelbige vi fri-er.

Chorus

3 Bayt-zhe mir oys a finf-un-tsvantsiger,
Oyf samerodno tsener,
Un shpilt-zhe mir klezmorimlech,
Dos zelbige noch shener.

Chorus

4 Bayt-zhe mir oys a finf-un-tsvantsiger,
Oyf same imperyaln,
Ich vel betn di klezmorimlech,
Zey zoln zich nit ayln.

Chorus

1 Change me this twenty-fiver,
Into equal pieces of three.
And play on, O bandsmen,
A merry tune for me.

2 Change me this twenty-fiver,
Into equal pieces of four.
And play on, O bandsmen,
The same you played before.

3 Change me this twenty-fiver,
Into equal pieces of ten.
And play on, O bandsmen,
The same, but better, again.

4 Change me this twenty-fiver,
Into equal coins—but no more—
And play on, O bandsmen,
The same tune, but much slower.

Biztu Mit Mir Broygez?

1   Biztu mit mir broygez?
Veys ich nit farvos—
Geyst arum a gantsn tog
Aropgelozt di noz.
    Ta di-day, day-day-day
    Ta di-day, day,
    Geyst arum a gantsn tog
    Aropgelozt di noz.

2   Un efsher vilstu visn
Az ich hob dich lib?
Lomir beyde ariberforn
Tsu dem gutn Yid.
    Ta di-day, day-day-day
    Ta di-day, day,
    Lomir beyde ariberforn
    Tsu dem gutn Yid.

3   Tsu a gutn Yidn
A pidyen im opgebn,
Zol er far undz Got betn
Oyf a gut lebn.
    Ta di-day, day-day-day
    Ta di-day, day,
    Zol er far undz Got betn
    Oyf a gut lebn.

4   Un az mir veln kumen
Tsurik fun gutn Yid,
Veln mir beyde ariberforn
In Zelve oyfn Yarid.
    Ta di-day, day-day-day
    Ta di-day, day,
    Veln mir beyde ariberforn
    In Zelve oyfn Yarid.

5   Dort vel ich dir koyfn
A zeyger mit a keyt,
Un a sheyne, groyse shtik
Zaydns oyf a kleyd.
    Ta di-day, day-day-day
    Ta di-day, day,
    Un a groyse, sheyne shtik
    Zaydns oyf a kleyd.

6   To, zay-zhe mer nit broygez,
Un greyt oyf gich tsum tish!
Un zets zich mit mir esn,
Bakumstu fun mir a kish!
    Ta di-day, day-day-day
    Ta di-day, day,
    Un zets zich mit mire esn
    Bakumstu fun mir a kish.

1 I don't know why you're angry,
And why you pout and frown,
And why you walk around all day
With your nose "hanging down."

2 Is it that you wish me
To prove that I love you?
If that is so, then let us go
Over to the "Pious Jew."

3 A token of our faith
We'll give to the Pious Jew,
So he can pray for a happy life
For me and for you.

4 And when we return
From our journey there,
Why then, we will just drop in
At the Zelva Fair!

5 At the fair I'll buy you
A handsome watch and chain.
And a large fine square of silk
For a dress and train.

6 So now don't you be angry
But set the table, please;
And sit right down and eat with me,
Then you may have a kiss!

Di Alte Kashe

Fregt di velt an al - te ka - she: Tra - di, tra - di - ri - di - rom?

Fregt di velt an al - te ka - she: Tra - di, tra - di - ri - di - rom?

En - fert men: tra - di - ri - di - rey - lom Tra - di!

Tra - di - ri - di - rom. Un az men vil, kon men doch zo - gn: Tra - di!

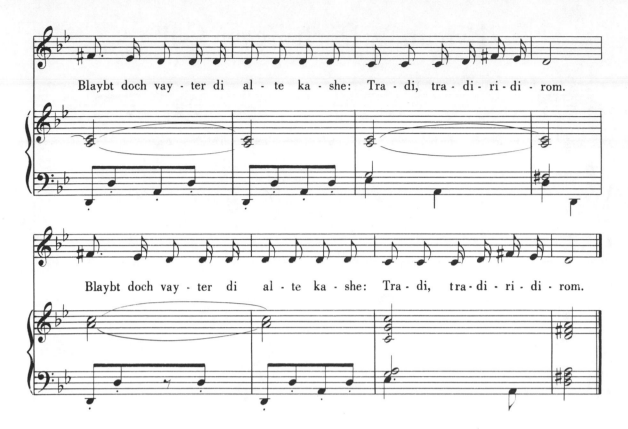

Blaybt doch vay - ter di al - te ka - she: Tra - di, tra - di - ri - di - rom.

Blaybt doch vay - ter di al - te ka - she: Tra - di, tra - di - ri - di - rom.

Fregt di velt an alte kashe:
Tradi, tradi-ridi-rom?

Un az men vil, kon men doch zogn :
Tra-di!

Enfert men: tradi-ridi-reylom—Tradi!
Tradi-ridi-rom . . .

Blaybt doch vayter di alte kashe:
Tradi, tradi-ridi-rom . . .

Men still ask the same old question:
Tradi, tradi-ridi-rom?

Or, if you will, you can counter:
Tra-di!

And they answer: tradi-ridi-reylom, Tradi!
Tradi-ridi-rom . . .

So, we're left with the same old question:
Tradi, tradi-ridi-rom . . .

121

Eynem Iz Doch Zeyer Gut

Quite slow, but with marked rhythm

Ey - nem is doch zey - er gut. Dem an - dern iz noch be - ser:

Trinkt er tey ___ mit ___ tsu - ker. ___

Trinkt er tey ___ mit ___ tsu - ker. Un

ich hob doch far - shpilt ___ may - ne yun - ge yo - rn,

Iz mir doch fin - ster un bi - ter. Un bi - ter.

2   Eynem iz doch zeyer gut,
Dem andern iz noch beser:
Geyt er sheyne kleyder.
Un ich hob doch farshpilt mayne yunge yorn,
Vi in a finstern cheyder.

3   Eynem iz doch zeyer gut,
Dem andern iz noch beser:
Flantst er zich a vayngortn.
Un ich hob doch farshpilt mayne yunge yorn,
Azoy vi a kartyozhnik in kortn.

1   Some people have an easy life,
Some have it even better,
And have sugar with their tea.
But I have lost my youth,
Oh. black misery!

2   Some people have an easy life,
Some have it even better,
And wear rich costumes.
But I have lost my youth,
As in a darkened room.

3   Some people have an easy life,
Some have it even better,
Planting themselves gardens.
But I have lost my youth,
Like a gambler at cards.

Zayt Gezunterheyt

Jewish soldier songs of the Pale stem from different periods. The oldest refer to the time of Nicholas I's recruitment law of 1827, which drafted young men into the army for a period of 25 years. This law was imposed upon all national minorities in the Russian empire. However, additional harsh measures were invoked against the Jews. This resulted in a period of horror referred to in Yiddish classical literature as the time of the *chaperlech* and the *kantonistn*, when young children of 12 were torn from their parents, sent into distant military camps and never heard from again. Even later, when Alexander II abolished this law in the seventies and military service was reduced to a period of four years, service in the Russian army was regarded with terror. At 21 a Jew was often married and military service meant leaving wife and children without any means of support, to serve a government that denied him a minimum of human rights. The three songs given here are from this latter period.

Melancholy

Zayt ge - zun - ter - heyt, may - ne li - be el - te - rn, Ich for fun aych a -
vek, in a vay - tn veg. Vu kayn vint vey - et nit Un

vu kayn foy-gl flit___ nit, Un vu kayn hon___ krey-et nit.

1 Zayt gezunterheyt, mayne libe eltern,
Ich for fun aych avek, in a vaytn veg.
Vu kayn vint veyet nit
Un vu kayn foygl flit nit
Un vu kayn hon kreyet nit.

2 Zayt gezunterheyt, mayne libe eltern,
Ich for fun aych avek, in a vaytn veg.
Got zol aych gebn
Gezunt un lebn,
Un mir a gliklichn veg.

1 Goodbye, my dear parents, goodbye,
I leave you now to journey far away.
Where no wind blows
And no bird flies
And no cock crows.

2 Goodbye, my dear parents, goodbye,
I leave you now to journey far away.
May God give you
Good health, long life,
And me an easy way.

Bak Mir Nit Kayn Bulkelech

Snappy

Bak mir nit kayn bul - ke - lech, Ich vel zey doch nit e - sn! Ich

for a - vek____ Fo - nyen di - nen, Vest in mir far - ge - sn!

Oy, ____ oy, ____ oy, ____ oy, ____ Yosh - ke fort a - vek! ____

Noch a sho un noch a sho__ Der poy - ezd geyt a - vek.

HE: 1 Bak mir nit kayn bulkelech,
Ich vel zey doch nit esn!
Ich for avek Fonyen* dinen,
Vest in mir fargesn!

Chorus:

> *Oy, oy, oy, oy, Yoshke fort avek!*
> *Noch a sho un noch a sho,*
> *Der poyezd geyt avek.*

SHE: 2 Koyf mir nit kayn lokenes,
Un mach mich nit sheyn!
Koyf dir a por shtivelech
Tsum priziv darfstu geyn.

Chorus:

> *Oy, oy, oy, oy, Yoshke fort avek!*
> *Lomir zich gezegenen*
> *Der poyezd geyt avek.*

HE: 3 Klog-zhe nit un veyn-zhe nit,
S'iz altsding blote!
Ich vel zayn by Fonyen
Der shenster in der rote!

Chorus:

> *Oy, oy, oy, oy, Yoshke fort avek!*
> *Noch a kush un noch a kush,*
> *Der poyezd geyt avek.*

SHE: 4 Di ban iz shoyn gekumen
Un es chapt mich on a shrek!
Oy vey Mamenyu,
Yoshke fort avek.

Chorus:

> *Oy, oy, oy, oy, Yoshke fort avek!*
> *Lomir zich gezegenen,*
> *Der poyezd geyt avek.*

1 Bake no sweet rolls for me,
I won't be here to eat them.
I'm off to serve the Czar,
You must forget me, sweet!
Oh, oh, oh, oh, Yoshke's got to go!
In another hour or so,
The train's about to go.

2 Buy no pretty "rats" for me,
With you gone, I'll be blue.
Buy yourself a pair of boots,
The barracks wait for you.
Oh, oh, oh, oh, Yoshke's got to go!
Let's say goodbye now,
The train's about to go.

3 Don't you cry and don't you sigh,
It's all a lot of rot.
I will be the handsomest
Soldier of the lot!
Oh, oh, oh, oh, Yoshke's got to go!
Let's kiss goodbye now,
The train's about to go.

4 The train has come into the yard,
Sweetheart, how I grieve!
Oh, oh, Mother dear—
Yoshke's about to leave.
Oh, oh, oh, oh, Yoshke's got to go!
Let's say our sad goodbyes,
The train's about to go.

* The Russian Czar: a derisive term used by East European Jews.

Forn Forstu Fun Mir Avek

Slow, poignant

Fo - rn for - stu fun mir a - vek, ___ tay-er__ le - bn__ mayns, Oy

fo - rn, for - stu ___ zich tsum pri - ziv shte - ln. Oy,

helf - zhe mir shoyn Go - te - nyu, zolst a - roys fun key - ser's

hent! Un der gan-tser pri -suts- tve zol-stu nit __ ge - fe - ln!

2 Vos-zhe hostu mir azoyns opgeton, tayer lebn
   mayns?
Vos ich benk azoy noch dir, oy noch dir?
Ich hob dir gornit opgeton, tayer lebn mayns,
Ich hob zich poshet ayngelibt in dir, oy in dir.

3 Forn forstu fun mir avek, tayer lebn mayns,
Fil taychn trern vel ich fargisn.
Oy, helf-zhe mir shoyn Gotenyu, zolst aroys fun
   keyser's hent!
Un mir zoln shoyn konen fun a chasene shmisn!

1 You are leaving me behind, my own true love,
To join the army, heaven protect you!
Oh help me, dear God, may you yet elude the Czar,
And all of the examiners reject you!

2 Oh, what have you done to me, my own true love,
   that I
Must long for you as much as I will long?
I didn't do a thing to you, my own true love,
I only fell in love with you, and that's not wrong!

3 You are leaving me behind, my own true love,
And oceans of tears will I be shedding.
Oh help me, dear God, may you yet elude the Czar,
And then we'll talk about our wedding!

A Geneyve

Bay mayn Re-bn iz ge-ve-zn, Iz ge-ve-zn, bay mayn Re-bn,

Bay mayn Re-bn, iz ge-ve-zn A ge-ney-ve!

Zi-bn hem-der vi di be-cher Dray mit la-tes, fir mit le-cher!

Bay mayn Re-bn iz ge-ve-zn a ge-ney-ve!

Chorus:

Bay mayn Rebn iz gevezn,
Iz gevezn, bay mayn Rebn,
Bay mayn Rebn, iz gevezn
A geneyve!

In my rabbi's house, there was—
It was in my rabbi's house—
In my rabbi's house, there was—
A robbery!

1 Zibn hemder vi di becher
Dray mit lates, fir mit lecher!
Bay mayn Rebn iz gevezn—a geneyve!

1 Seven fancy shirts like moles,
Three with patches, four with holes!
In my rabbi's house there was—a robbery!

Chorus

2 Zibn laychter vi di shtern,
Dray on fis un fir on rern!
Bay mayn Rebn iz gevezn—a geneyve!

2 Seven candlesticks like rockets,
Three no sticks and four no sockets!
In my rabbi's house there was—a robbery!

Chorus

3 Zibn hener vi di tsigl
Dray on kep un fir on fligl!
Bay mayn Rebn iz gevezn—a geneyve!

3 Seven rooster-hens like kings,
Three no heads and four no wings!
In my rabbi's house there was—a robbery!

Chorus

4 Zibn meydn vi di sosnes,
Dray on tseyn un fir on yosles!
Bay mayn Rebn iz gevezn—a geneyve!

4 Seven pretty girls like plums,
Three no teeth and four no gums!
In my rabbi's house there was—a robbery!

Oyf Dem Yam Veyet A Vintele

This old love song has been included in this section because it is sometimes sung as a humorous song in this way:

Oyf dem yam veyet a vi-vi-vintl, veyet a vi-vi-vintl,
Un di chvalyes shlo-vo-vo-gn,
Ch'ob zich farli-ebt in a sheyn yingele
Un hob nit far vemen tsu zo-vo-vo-gn . . .

Sung thus, it is quite comical.

For comic version, play accompaniment rhythmically, with a hurdy-gurdy effect and with no pedal.
For romantic version, play accompaniment soft and legato with pedal.

132

1 Oyf dem yam veyet a vintele, veyet a vintele,
Un di chvalyes shlogn.
Ch'ob zich farlibt in a sheyn yingele,
Ch'ob nit far vemen tsu zogn.

2 Ich hob zich gebovet a shtibele in vald, a
   shtibele in vald,
Arum un arum mit fenster.
Fun ale kartinkes vos ich hob gezen,
Biztu bay mir der shenster!

3 Tsu libstu mich fun tifn hartsn, fun tifn hartsn,
Tsu libstu nor mayn sheyn ponim?
Du host mich gor avekgekoylet—
Azoy vi di rechte gazlonim!

4 Az a gazlen koylet a mentshn, koylet a mentshn,
Koylet er im mit a meser—
Du host mich gekoylet, un nit derkoylet,
Du bizt fun a gazlen noch greser!

1 A breeze is blowing across the sea,
The waves are rising high.
I have fallen in love with a handsome lad,
And there's no one to hear my cry.

2 I have built me a hut in the forest green,
With a window in every wall.
Of all the views I ever have seen,
You're the fairest of all.

3 Oh, do you love me with all your heart,
Or is it just my pretty head?
Like a real black murderer—
You have slain me dead!

4 When a murderer slays a man,
He slays him with a knife.
You have slain me, and not slain me—
Leaving me half my life!

Sha, Shtil, Macht Nisht Kayn Geruder!

Chorus:

Sha, shtil, macht nisht kayn geruder!
Der Rebe geyt shoyn tantsn vider.
Sha, shtil, macht nish kayn gevald!
Der Rebe geyt shoyn tantsn bald.

1   Un az der Rebe tantst,
Tantsn doch vi vent;
Lomir ale
Plyesken mit di hent!

   Chorus

2   Un az der Rebe tantst,
Tantst doch mit, der tish;
Lomir ale
Tupen mit di fis!

   Chorus

3   Un az der Rebe zingt
Dem heylign nign,
Blaybt der Sotn
A toyter lign.

   Chorus

Quiet, be still! Make no commotion!
Now's the rabbi's turn to dance!
Quiet! be still! Stop the chatter!
The rabbi's about to dance!

1   And when the rabbi dances,
The very walls do leap.
So, let's all of us,
Stamp with our feet!

2   When the rabbi dances,
The very table reels.
So, let's all of us,
Pound with our heels!

3   And when the rabbi chants
His holy melody,
He sends the Devil
To his misery!

Kum Aher, Du Filozof

1 Kum aher, du filozof,
Mit dayn ketsisłn moychl;
Kum aher tsum Rebn's tish
Un lern zich dort seychl!

Chorus:

Babim-babam, babim-babam,
Babim-babam, bam, bimbam.

2 A damf-shif hostu oysgetracht
Un nemst zich mit dem iber.
Der Rebe shpreyt zayn tichl oys
Un shpant dem yam ariber!

Chorus

3 A luft-balon hostu oysgeklert
Un meynst du bizt a choretz.
Der Rebe shpot, der Rebe lacht,
Er darf es oyf kapores!

Chorus

4 Tsu veystu vos der Rebe tut
Ven er zitst b'yechides?
In eyn minut in himl flit
Un est dort sholesh-sudes!*

Chorus

1 Come, my fine philosopher,
You're a trifle dense;
Come to rabbi's table here,
And get a little sense.

2 You thought up the steamship and
You think it quite a notion.
Our rabbi spreads his kerchief out
And floats across the ocean!

3 So now you've dreamed up the balloon,
And think you're very spry;
Our rabbi scoffs, our rabbi laughs,
Who needs such things to fly?

4 For when our rabbi's all alone
And tight-shut doors exclude us,
At once he flies up to the sky
And there eats "sholesh-sudes".

*Sholesh-sudes: Whether or not the Jew of the Pale ate at all during the week, on the Sabbath it was his *duty* to eat thrice. Shalosh-S'udot was the third meal.

HOLIDAY SONGS

THE HOLIDAYS have remained important institutions in the life of the Jewish people. Over the centuries, they have undergone a process of development and change, both in the rituals and customs. These in turn are observed differently in the various Jewish communities of the world. Thus, the Jewish store of holiday songs is exceedingly colorful and diverse.

The majority of the holiday songs are religious in conception. Nevertheless, a number of secular songs have sprung up in many Jewish communities of modern times. The diverse manner of treating the holiday material is evident, even in the limited number of songs given here. *Simchu na* is different from *Kinder mir hobn Simches Toyre*; *Mi Y'malel* varies from *Chanuke, O, Chanuke*; the hasidic *Yis'm'chu Adirim* departs considerably from the Israeli *Bikurim*.

In modern Israel, holiday songs have assumed a new character. Marked by an increased joyousness, they stress the argicultural nature of many ancient holidays.

Shabbat Hamalka

Text: Ch. N. Bialik

Tune: F. Minkovsky

Ha - cha - ma ___ mey - rosh ha - i - la - not ___ nis - tal - ka,

Bo - u v' ney - tsey lik - rat Shab - bat ___ ha - mal - ka. Hi -

ney hi yo - re - det ha - kdo - sha, ___ ha - bru - cha, V'

i - ma ma - la - chim ___ tsva sha - lom ___ u - m' nu - cha. Bo

1 Hachama meyrosh ha-ilanot nistalka,
Bo-u v'neytsey likrat Shabbat hamalka.
Hiney hi yoredet hakdosha, habrucha,
V'ima malachim tsva shalom um'nucha.
    Bo-i, bo-i, hamalka. Bo-i, bo-i, hakala.
    Shalom aleychem malachey hashalom.

2 Kibalnu p'ney Shabbat birnana, utfila,
Habayta nashuva b'lev maley gila.
'Sham aruch hashulchan, haneyrot ya-iru,
Kol pinot habayit yiz'rachu, yaz'hiru.
    Shabbat shalom, um'vorach, Shabbat shalom,
       um'vorach.
    Bo-achem l'shalom, malachey hashalom.

3 Shvi, zaka, imanu uv zivech na ori,
Layla v'yom achar ta-avori,
Va-anachnu n'chabdech b'vigdey chamudot
Bizmirot ut'filot, uv'shalosh s'udot.
    Uvimnucha sh'leyma, uvimnucha n'ima,
    Barchuni l'shalom, malachey hashalom.

4 Hachama meyrosh ha-ilanot nistalka,
B-ou un'lave et Shabbat hamalka.
Tseyteych l'shalom, hakdosha, hazaka,
D'i, sheyshet yamim el shuvech n'chake.
    Ken l'Shabbat haba-a, ken l'Shabbat haba-a,
    Tsetchem l'shalom, malachey hashalom.

1 The sun has slipped behind the trees,
Come, let us greet the Sabbath Queen.
She is now descending, the holy one,
Surrounded by gentle angels of peace.
    She comes, the Queen. She comes, the Bride.
    Greetings to you, O angels of peace.

2 We greet the Sabbath with song and prayer,
Entering the house, our hearts full of gladness.
The table is decked, the candles are lit,
Every corner sparkles with shining cleanness.
    Peace to the Sabbath, blessed be she,
    Peace unto you, O angels of peace.

3 O beauteous one, with rays of shining light,
A night and a day—and then you depart;
We receive you adorned in raiment so fine,
With prayer and song, with feasting and wine.
 O peace so sweet, O peace complete,
 Give us your blessing, O angels of peace.

4 The sun has hidden behind the trees,
Come, let us bid farewell to the Queen.
Depart in peace, O blessed one,
Six whole days, we shall be awaiting you.
 Till the coming Sabbath, the coming Sabbath,
 Depart in peace, O angels of peace.

Shabes Licht Un Shabes Lompn

Tune: Joel Engel

Shabes licht un shabes lompn, O, vi zis iz ayer shayn!

Shabes, O Shabes, O heyliger Shabes!

Vifil brengt er treyst dem Yidn In zayn elnt in zayn payn.

1 Shabes licht un shabes lompn,
O, vi zis iz ayer shayn!
Shabes, O Shabes, O heyliger Shabes!
Vifil brengt er treyst dem Yidn
In zayn elnt in zayn payn.
Shabes, O Shabes, O heyliger Shabes!

2 Kumt tsu undz der Shabes koydesh,
Vi es vern licht gebentsht,
Shabes, O Shabes, O heyliger Shabes!
Bald antloyft di more-sh'choyre,
Un men vert a nayer mentsh.
Shabes, O Shabes, O heyliger Shabes!

Chorus:

Day-di-di, day-dam, day-day-day,
Day-di-di, day-dam, day-day-day
Day-di-di, day-dam, day-day,
Day-di-di, day-dam, dam.

143

1 Sabbath candles, Sabbath lamps,
Oh, how pleasant is your glow!
Sabbath, O Sabbath, O holy Sabbath!
What comfort your light brings the Jew,
In his misery and woe!
Sabbath, O Sabbath, O holy Sabbath!

2 When the holy Sabbath comes,
And the candle lights are blessed,
Sabbath, O Sabbath, O holy Sabbath!
All melancholy disappears,
And men's spirits are at rest,
Sabbath, O Sabbath, O holy Sabbath!

Shabes Beyn Hashmoshes

Text: B. Kovner

Tune: Joel Engel

Es geyt shoyn a - vek zich der hey - li - ger Sha - bes In shti - bl vert fin - ster, in shti - bl iz shtil. Es shep - tchet di ma - me: "Ach Got fun A - vrom",

144

Zi shep-tchet di t'fi-le mit harts __ un ge-fil.

2 "Ach Got fun Avrom, fun Yitschok, fun
      Yankev,
Farnem doch mayn t'file in himls getselt,
Un shik mir parnose, un richt oyf mayn mazl,
Un lichtig zol vern mayn finstere velt."

3 Es dunklt der himl, es tsi-en zich volkns,
In shtibl iz finster un umetig shtil,
Nor ergets in vinkl, farshtupt in a shpare,
Dort tshirket un tshirket farborgn a gril.

1 The Sabbath will soon be all over and gone,
The room is so quiet, as darkness draws near.
"O God of our Fathers," the mother murmurs,
She murmurs her prayer, heartfelt and sincere.

2 "O God of Abraham, and Isaac and Jacob,
Accept Thou my prayer in Thy heavenly height,
Oh, send me my livelihood, make my lot easy,
My world is so dark, may it yet become bright!"

3 The heaven grows darker with gathering clouds,
The room is quite dark and so sad and so still,
Somewhere in a corner, stuck away in a crack,
A cricket is chirping and chirping at will.

Lama Sukka Zu?

Sukkot Song

Israelis will recognize in this tune that of another folksong, "Shir Shel Notrim" (The Song of the Watchmen), which was sung in the early days of the settlement of Eretz Israel.

Playful

La - ma suk - ka zu, A - ba tov she - li?

Slightly slower

Ley - shev ba - suk - ka, ya - ki - ri, Ley - shev ba - suk - ka, cha - vi - vi,

Ley - shev ba - suk - ka, ye - led cheyn, ___ Ye - led cheyn she - li.

Ley - shev ba - suk - ka, ye - led cheyn, ____ Ye - led cheyn she - li.

2 Lama leyshev ba, aba tov sheli?
Avoteynu, yakiri,
Avoteynu, chavivi,
Avoteynu af gam heyma
Yashvu basukka.

3 Ma bakufsa yesh, aba tov sheli?
Etrog, etrog, yakiri,
Etrog, etrog, chavivi,
Etrog, etrog, yeled cheyn,
Yeled cheyn sheli.

1 What is this hut for, daddy dear?
This hut's to sit in, sonny dear,
This hut's to sit in, bunny dear,
This hut's to sit in, my sweet lad,
O darling lad of mine!

2 Why sit in it, daddy dear?
Because our fathers, sonny dear,
Because our fathers, bunny dear,
Because our fathers, even they,
Sat in this hut too.

3 What's in this box, daddy dear?
A citron's in it, sonny dear,
A citron's in it, bunny dear,
A citron's in it, my sweet lad,
O darling lad of mine!

Simchu Na

With restrained joy
Chorus

Simchat Torah Song

Yemenite Melody

Sim - chu na, ____ sim - chu na, ____ B' sim - chat __ ha - To - ra.

Sim - chu na, ____ sim - chu na, ____ B' sim - chat __ ha - To - ra.

Fine

Yis - m' - chu ____ a - hu - vim ____ B' sim - chat __ ha - To - ra.

Yis - m' chu ____ a - hu - vim ____ B' sim - chat __ ha - To - ra.

D. C. al Fine

Chorus:

Simchu na, simchu na,
B'simchat haTora.
Simchu na, simchu na,
B'simchat haTora.

1   Yis'mchu ahuvim
B'simchat haTora.
Yism'chu ahuvim
B'simchat haTora.

   Chorus

2   Yis'mchu b'ruchim
B'simchat haTora.
Yism'chu b'ruchim
B'simchat haTora.

   Chorus

3   Yism'chu giborim
B'simchat haTora.
Yism'chu giborim
B'simchat haTora.

   Chorus

Let us rejoice, let us rejoice,
In the joy of the Torah.

1   Rejoice, ye beloved,
Who love the Torah.

2   Rejoice, ye blessed ones,
In the joy of the Torah.

3   Rejoice, ye brave men,
In the joy of the Torah.

149

Kinder, Mir Hobn Simches Toyre!

Text and Tune: Morris Warshavsky

Kin - der, mir ho - bn Simches Toy - re,

Sim - ches Toy - re oyf der gan - tser velt. Toy - re iz di bes - te s'choy - re,

A - zoy hot der Re - be mit undz ge - knelt.

Chorus

Oy, vey, oy - oy - oy, Frey - lech kin - der, ot a - zoy!

Rend - lech shit - n zich fun di zek, Frey - lech____ on an ek!

2 Chotsh ich bin mir an orim Yidl,
Un es dart mir gut der moych.
Simches Toyre, zing ich a lidl,
Un mach a gute koyse oych!

Chorus

3 Ver se kon nit mayne tsores,
Zol zey nit konen, zog ich aych;
Nor take, glaych mit ale s'rores,
Bin ich im Simches Toyre raych!

Chorus

4 Dvoyre, gib mir di naye kapote,
Ich vel zi onton take atsind,
Ich vel dir zogn, altsding iz blote,
Abi men iz borech-hashem gezint!

Chorus

5 Vu iz Berl? Vu iz Dvosye?
Ruf zey ale in shtub arayn!
Di mume Sose, dem feter Yose,
Zoln zey ale freylech zayn!

Chorus

6 Oy vey Dvoyre, vos hostu moyre?
Ch'bin abisl freylech, ch'ken nit shteyen?
Dvoyre-lebn, um Simches Toyre,
Ver iz nit freylech, zog aleyn!

Chorus:

Oh vey, oy-oy-oy,
Freylech kinder, ot azoy!
Rendlech shitn zich fun di zek,
Freylech—on an ek!

1 Children, we'll have a celebration,
Simchas Torah is here today.
"Torah is the best occupation,"
That's what our rabbi used to say.

Oh, Oh, hey, hey, hey,
Let's be merry, that's the way,
From the sacks the coins roll out—
Laugh and sing and shout!

2 Though I am just a simple fellow,
And my worries are never through,
Simchas Torah—I am quite mellow—
I sing and take a drink or two.

3 I have such troubles, it's not funny,
May you never know of them, I pray,
But just like folks with lots of money,
I'm rich on Simchas Torah day!

4 Dvoyre, give me my brand new frockcoat,
I'll put it on like a man of wealth,
Let me tell you, nothing else matters,
If with God's help, you have your health!

5 Where is Berl? Where is Dvosye?
Get all of them here, every one,
Get Aunt Sosye and Uncle Yosye,
Let everybody have some fun!

6 Come, come, Dvoyre, no need to worry,
If I'm a bit merry and cannot stand.
But Dvoyre darling, on Simchas Torah,
Everyone is merry! Do you understand?

151

Mi Y'malel?

This is sung during Chanukkah, which celebrates the victory of the Macca-
bees over the Syrian king, Antiochus, 165 B.C.E. It may be sung as a round,
with the second group coming in at the end of the second line.

Mi y'malel g'vurot Yisrael?
Otan mi yimne?

Hen b'chol dor yakum hagibor
Go-el ha-am.

Shma: Bayamim hahem baz'man haze,
Makkabi moshi-a ufode.
Uv'yameynu, kol am Yisrael,
Yitached yakum l'higa-el!

Repeat first four lines

Who can retell your feats, Israel?
Who can count them all?

Throughout the years, a hero appears,
To save us. Recall:

At this very time so long ago,
Maccabee arose and smote the foe.
The whole people in our time as well,
Will unite and build free Israel.

153

Chanuke, O Chanuke!

Text: M. Rivesman

Hasidic Melody

Got far di ni - sim, Un kumt gi - cher tan - tsn in kon!

1   Chanuke, O Chanuke, a yontev a sheyner,
A lustiger, a freylicher, nito noch azoyner!
Ale nacht in dreydl shpiln mir,
Zudig-heyse latkes esn mir.

Chorus:

   Geshvinder, tsindt kinder,
   Di dininke lichtelech on.
   Zogt 'Al-hanisim," loybt Got far di nisim,
   Un kumt gicher tantsn in kon!

2   Yehuda hot fartribn dem soyne, dem rotseyach,
Un hot in Beys-hamikdesh gezungen
   "Lamnatseyach",
Di shtot Yerusholayim hot vider oyfgelebt,
Un tsu a nayem lebn hot yederer geshtrebt.

Chorus:

   Deriber, dem giber,
   Yehuda Makabi loybt hoych!
   Zol yeder bazunder, bazingen di vunder,
   Un libn dos folk zolt ir oych!

1   Chanukkah, O Chanukkah, O holiday so fair,
So happy and so merry, there's none can compare.
We spin the dreydl-top, every night,
Red-hot pancakes do we eat.

   Come children, we'll light
   The thin, little candles you see.
   For the salvation of a grateful nation,
   Thank God, and dance merrily!

2   Maccabee defeated and cast out the cruel enemy,
And in the Holy Temple sang hymns of victory,
The city of Jerusalem revived and grew,
And everyone began to build his life anew.

   Come children, prepare for
   A real tribute to the Maccabee.
   Let us all sing of the victory
   And a people so brave and so free.

155

Hayo, Haya

Chanukkah Song

2 Ba el ir Yerushalayim, Yerushalayim,
Shama shafach dam kamayim, dam kamayim.
Group: Mi hu? *Solo:* Anti-ochus, Anti-ochus.
Group: Anti-ochus, Anti-ochus.

3 Ba v'saraf et haTora, et haTora,
Kiba neyrot shel ham'nora, shel ham'nora.
Group: Mi hu? *Solo:* Anti-ochus, Anti-ochus.
Group: Anti-ochus, Anti-ochus.

4 Kam ish gibor, shmo Yehuda, shmo Yehuda,
Hitsil artso hachamuda, hachamuda.
Group: Mi hu? *Solo:* Hamakkabi, Hamakkabi.
Group: Hamakkabi, Hamakkabi.

5 Ba l'mikdash, hidlik m'nora, hidlik m'nora,
V'lay'hudim hayta ora, hayta ora.
Group: Matay? *Solo:* baChanukka, baChanukka.
Group: baChanukka, baChanukka!

1 Once there was a wicked, wicked king,
His sword was sharp, his darts did sting.
What was his name?—Anti-ochus!

2 He came to Jerusalem's holy quarter,
And shed our blood like water, water.
What was his name?—Anti-ochus!

3 He came and burned the Torah, Torah,
Put out the Menorah, the Menorah.
What was his name?—Anti-ochus!

4 Rose the hero, Judah the brave,
His ancient land to save, to save.
What was his name?—the Maccabee!

5 In the Temple he lit the Menorah, Menorah,
And then the Jews had light, had Torah.
When was this?—On Chanukkah!

Ki Tavo-u El Ha-Arets

Tu Bishvat Song

1 Ki tavo-u el ha-arets
Un-tatem kol ets t'chila,
V'natan ha-ets piryo,
V'ha-arets y'vula.

1 And when you come unto the land,
May you forthwith plant trees.
And the trees will bear fruit,
And the earth will blossom forth.

Chorus:
  Eyt linto-a ilanot,
  Eyt linto-a v'livnot.

This is the time for planting,
This is the time for building.

2 Vishavtem ish tachat gafno,
V'tachat t'eynato,
Vihyitem k'ets shatul
Al palgey mayim.

2 And each will sit under his grapevine,
And each will rest under his fig tree,
And you will be like unto the trees
Planted beside the water.

3 Uv'nitem charvot olam
Shom'mot t'komemu,
Vichyitem al admatchem
Lavetach ul'olam.

3 And you will rebuild the silent
Ruins of the earth,
And live upon your land,
Rooted, and for all time.

Haynt Iz Purim, Brider!

Text: M. Rivesman

Melody: A. Goldfaden

Haynt iz Purim, brider,
Es iz der yontev groys.
Lo mir zin gen lider,
Geyn fun hoyz tsu hoyz.
Lach, Mor dche le lach,
A yon tev l mach, Kind's
kin der ge den ken dem nes!____ Zingt bri der lech, zingt, Tantst
frey lech un shpringt, Dem tay er n tog nit far gest.____

1 Haynt iz Purim, brider,
S'iz der yontev groys.
Lomir zingen lider,
Geyn fun hoyz tsu hoyz.
Lach, Mordchele lach,
A yontevl mach,
Kind's kinder gedenken dem nes!
Zingt briderlech, zingt,
Tantst freylech un shpringt,
Dem tayern tog nit fargest.

2 Homen iz a roshe,
Dos veyst yeder Yid.
Ober Got, nishkoshe,
Shvaygt dem roshe nit.
Vart Homenke, vart,
Du zay nit genart,
A nes hot geton mit undz Got.
Zingt briderlech, zingt,
Tanst freylech un shpringt,
Macht greser un greser dem rod!

Repeat first four lines

1 Today is Purim, brothers,
Best holiday of them all.
Let's sing and play, brothers,
At each house we'll call.
Mordecai, be gay,
Have a holiday,
We relive this every year.
Sing, my brothers, sing,
Dance and have your fling!
Never forget this day so dear.

2 Haman is a bad man,
All of us agree.
God won't let this madman
Get away scotfree.
Wait, Haman wait,
You'll meet your fate,
We were saved by the Holy One,
Sing, my brothers, sing,
Dance and have your fling!
Let all of us join in the fun!

Hop! Mayne Homntashn!

1 Yachne-Dvoshe fort in mark,
Zi halt zich in eyn pakn,
Fort oyf Purim koyfn mel,
Homntashn bakn.

1 Yachne-Dvoshe's in a dither,
Packing for the market-place,
She is off to buy the flour
For to bake the Purim cakes.

Chorus:

Hop! mayne homntashn,
Hop! mayne vayse.
Hop! mit mayne homntashn
Hot pasirt a mayse!

Ho, my homentashn!
Ho, my white delights!
Ho, my homentashn
Didn't come out quite right!

2   S'geyt a regn, s'geyt a shney,
Es kapet fun di decher.
Yachne firt shoyn korn-mel,
In a zak mit lecher.

2   It's raining and it's snowing,
And the roofs are dripping,
Yachne's bringing cornmeal home
In a bag that's ripping.

   Chorus

3   Nisht kayn honig, nisht kayn mon,
Un fargesn heyvn,
Yachne macht shoyn homntashn,
Es bakt zich shoyn in oyvn . . .

3   She's brought no honey, no poppy-seed,
And quite forgot the yeast.
But Yachne's making homentashn
They're in the oven, at least.

   Chorus

4   Yachne trogt shoyn shalach-mones,
Tsu der bobe Yente—
Tsvey-dray homntashn,
Halb-roy—halb-farbrente!

4   Yachne's carrying her Purim gift
To her mother-in-law,
Two or three homentashn,
Half-burned and half-raw.

   Chorus

Yom L'yabasha (Shir Hag'ula)

Text: Judah ha-Levi

Passover Song.

Chad Gadya

The "Chad Gadya" song given here, in a version used by the Bessarabian Hasidim, is sung at the Seder ceremony; the text is said to have originated in Western Europe. This kind of cumulative song is to be found in virtually every European country. The Siamese are said to have such a song. In our own country the Pennsylvania Dutch sing a song of this kind called "Der Bauer shickt den Jokel aus." The English "House That Jack Built" is a well-known children's song here and in Canada.

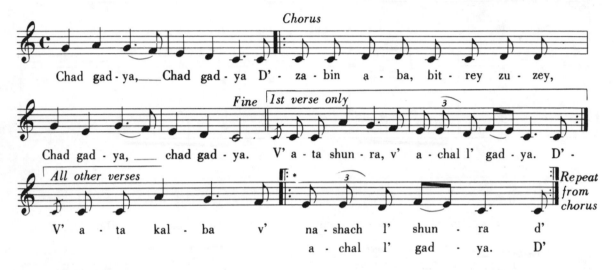

*The additional lines in the remaining verses are sung to this measure.

Chad gadya, chad gadya,

Chorus:

   D'zabin aba bitrey zuzey,
   Chad gadya, chad gadya.

1 V'ata shunra, v'achal l'gadya, [*Chorus*]

2 V'ata kalba, v'nashach l'shunra,
D'achal l'gadya, [*Chorus*]

3 V'ata chutra, v'hika l'kalba,
D'nashach l'shunra, d'achal l'gadya, [*Chorus*]

4 V'ata nura, v'saraf l'chutra,
D'hika l'kalba, d'nashach l'shunra,
D'achal l'gadya, [*Chorus*]

An only kid, an only kid.

That father bought for two zuzim;
An only kid, an only kid.

1 Then came the cat and ate the kid, *etc.*

2 Then came the dog and bit the cat,
That ate the kid, *etc.*

3 Then came the stick and beat the dog,
That bit the cat that ate the kid, *etc.*

4 Then came the fire and burnt the stick
That hit the dog that bit the cat
That ate the kid, *etc.*

5   V'ata maya, v'chava l'nura,
D'saraf l'chutra, d'hika l'kalba,
D'nashach l'shunra, d'achal l'gadya, [Chorus]

6   V'ata tora, v'shata l'maya,
D'chava l'nura, d'saraf l'chutra,
D'hika l'kalba, d'nashach l'shunra,
D'achal l'gadya, [Chorus]

7   V'ata shochet, v'shachat l'sora,
D'shata l'maya, d'chava l'nura,
D'saraf l'chutra, d'hika l'kalba,
D'nashach l'shunra, d'achal l'gadya, [Chorus]

8   V'ata Malach Hamavet, v'shachat l'shochet,
D'shachat l'sora, d'shata l'maya,
D'chava l'nura, d'saraf l'chutra,
D'hika l'kalba, d'nashach l'shunra,
D'achal l'gadya, [Chorus]

9   V'ata Hakadosh Baruch-hu,
V'shachat l'Malach Hamavet,
D'shachat l'shochet, d'shachat l'sora,
D'shata l'maya, d'chava l'nura,
D'saraf l'chutra, d'hika l'kalba,
D'nashach l'shunra, d'achal l'gadya,
D'zabin aba, bitrey zuzey,
Chad gadya, chad gadya!

5   Then came the water and quenched the fire,
That burnt the stick that beat the dog,
That bit the cat that ate the kid, etc.

6   Then came the ox and drank the water,
That quenched the fire that burnt the stick,
That beat the dog that bit the cat,
That ate the kid, etc.

7   Then came the butcher and slew the ox,
That drank the water, that quenched the fire,
That burnt the stick that beat the dog,
That bit the cat that ate the kid, etc.

8   Then came the Angel of Death and killed the butcher,
That slew the ox, that drank the water,
That quenched the fire that burnt the stick,
That beat the dog that bit the cat,
That ate the kid, etc.

9   Then came the Lord, Blessed be he,
And destroyed the Angel of Death,
That killed the butcher, that slew the ox,
That drank the water that quenched the fire,
That burnt the stick that beat the dog,
That bit the cat that ate the kid,
That father bought for two zuzim,
An only kid, an only kid!

Ashrey Ha-Ish

During Lag B'Omer pious Jews make a pilgrimage to Safed to visit the tomb of Rabbi Shimon bar Yochay, to whom popular tradition ascribes the authorship of the Zohar, the central work of the Kabbalah.

Ash - rey ha - ish she - lo cha - ta, Tsa - dik hu, v' cha -

sid ku - lo. V' - im cha - ta, yesh gam s' - li - cha, V' -

nis - lach lo, v' ___ nim - chal lo. Ash - rey - nu, Ma tov chel - key - nu,

Rab - bi Shi - mon ___ bar Yo - chay. bar Yo - chay.

Ashrey ha-ish shelo chata,
Tsadik hu, v'chasid kulo.
V'im chata, yesh gam s'licha,
V'nislach lo, v'nimchal lo.

Ashreynu,
Ma tov chelkeynu,
Rabbi Shimon bar Yochay.

Happy the man who has not sinned,
For he is virtuous and just.
If he should sin, there still is grace,
And he will be absolved, we trust.

Blessed are we,
How goodly our fate,
Rabbi Shimon bar Yochay.

Bikurim

Text: Sh. Bass

Tune: Sara Levy

P'ri ga - ni hi - ney he - vey - ti, M'lo ha - te - ne rav p' er,

Bi - ku - rim po he - e - ley - ti, V' ro - shi i - tar - ti zer.

La - la - la la la la la la la la la la la

la la la la la la la la. la.

2 Min hakfar movil ha-ira,
Benro-im tale ug'di,
V'shirav b'kol yashira,
Didl-didl-didl-di.
Li-li-li . . .

3 Ben ikar mipri ganehu,
T'eynim v'rimonim,
Uvasal lo al shichmeyhu,
T'himena zug yonim.
Lu-lu-lu . . .

1 Here I bring my garden's crop,
A basket full of all good things,
First of fruit I bear upon
My head with flowers ringed.
La-la-la . . .

2 From the village to the city,
A shepherd leads his lamb and kid
Loudly sings this pleasant ditty,
Didl-didl-didl-di.
Li-li-li . . .

3 A farmer bearing dates and figs
And pomegranates too,
While in the basket on his back
A pair of sweet doves coo.
Lu-lu-lu . . .

Yis'm'chu Adirim

Shavuot Song

Yis'-m'-chu a-di-rim, a-di-rim, B'-sim-chat ma-tan To-ra. B'-sim-chat ma-tan To-ra. B'-sim-chat ma-tan To-ra. Gi-la, ri-na, di-tsa, v'-ched-va, B'-sim-chat ma-tan To-ra.__ Gi-la, ri-na, di-tsa, v'-ched-va, B'-

| Yis'm'chu adirim, adirim, | Rejoice, O ye mighty men, |
| B'simchat matan Tora. | In the great gift of the Torah. |

| Gila, rina, ditsa v'chedva, | Joy, oh joy, oh great joy, |
| B'simchat matan Tora. | In the great gift of the Torah. |

| Tora ya-a, Tora na-a, | Torah the beautiful, Torah the lovely, |
| Moshe kibel miSinay. | Given to Moses at the mountainside. |

Al Naharot Bavel

Al naharot Bavel bachinu sham,	By the rivers of Babylon we wept,
B'zochreynu et Tsiyon.	Remembering Zion.
Al aravim b'tocha talinu kinoroteynu.	Upon the willows we hung up our harps.
Eych nashir al admat neychar?	Oh, how could we sing in a strange land?

The above song is based on Psalm 137.

PARTISAN SONGS

A GROUP of songs composed during the catastrophic years of the Second World War sound the note of horror of those years: songs of the concentration camp, satiric songs full of hatred of the enemy, documentary ballads describing the hunger, exposure, inhuman labor, beatings, degradation and —finally—gas chambers, the Hebrew chants of Jews going to their death. But side by side with these we also hear the ringing songs of defiance of the Jewish Partisans. These songs, arising spontaneously out of the sufferings of the people, became known to Jews of many lands, for into the concentration camps were driven Jews from every corner of Europe.

S'dremlen Feygl Oyf Di Tsvaygn

The text of this cradle song was written by the young poet Leah Rudnitzky, born in Kalvaria, Lithuania, in 1916. The shooting of some 4,000 Jews on April 5, 1943, on Ponar, left a lasting impression on the sensitive poet. A three-year-old child was saved from the massacre, for whom she wrote this lullaby. When the Vilna ghetto was liquidated, Leah Rudnitzky was sent "left"—toward Maidanek—and never afterward heard of.

The tune is obviously borrowed from the lullaby written by Yampolsky.

176

zingt: Lu - lu, lu - lu, lu.

2 S'iz dayn vigl vu geshtanen,
Oysgeflochtn fun glik.
Un dayn mame, oy dayn mame,
Kumt shoyn keynmol nit tsurik!
Lu-lu, lu-lu, lu . . .

3 Ch'ob gezen dayn tatn loyfn
Unter hogl fun shteyn—
Iber felder iz gefloygn
Zayn faryosemter geveyn.
Lu-lu, lu-lu, lu . . .

1 Birds are sleeping on the branches,
Sleep, my darling baby.
In the dugout, near your cradle,
Sits a stranger, crooning.
Lu-lu, lu-lu, lu . . .

2 Garlanded with loving dreams,
Elsewhere once you lay.
But your mother, oh, your mother,
Never will return today!
Lu-lu, lu-lu, lu . . .

3 I have seen your father running
Through a hail of stones,
And across the fields there drifted
His melancholy groans.
Lu-lu, lu-lu, lu . . .

Yugnt–Hymn

Basya Rubin composed this melody during the war. Later, in the Vilna ghetto, the poet Sh. Kacerginski wrote words to it for the ghetto youth club.

Text: Sh. Kacerginski

Tune: Basya Rubin

Und · zer lid iz ful mit troy · er, Drayst iz und · zer mun · ter · gang! Chotsh der soy · ne vacht baym toy · er, Shtu · rimt yu · gnt mit ge · zang! Yung iz

ye - der, ye - der, ye - der ver es vil nor Yo - rn

ho - bn kayn ba - dayt; Al - te ke - nen, ke - nen, ke - nen oych zayn

kin - der Fun a na - yer, fray - er tsayt!

2 Ver es voglt oyf di vegn,
Ver mit draystkayt shtelt zayn fus,
Brengt di yugnt zey antkegn
Funem geto, a gerus!

Chorus

3 Mir gedenken ale sonim,
Mir gedenken ale fraynt.
Eybik veln mir dermonen
Undzer nechtn mitn haynt.

Chorus

4 Kloybn mir tsunoyf di glider
Vider shtoln mir di rey.
Geyt a boyer, geyt a shmider,
Lomir ale geyn mit zey!

Chorus

1 Though our song be full of sorrow,
Yet our stride is bold and strong.
Though the foe be at the gate,
Youth will storm it with a song.

Every, everyone who wills it, can be young,
There's no point to counting age;
Old folks can be, yes, they can be children too,
Of a new and happy age.

2 All those wandering on the highways,
All those marching boldly out,
Youth comes pouring from the ghetto
Forth to meet them with a shout!

3 We remember all who love us,
We remember all who hate;
We will guard in our hearts
The past and the present date.

4 Now we gather up our remnants,
Steel our ranks, march on together,
With the builders and the welders,
Brothers, let us march together!

Partizaner Lid

In 1942 Itzik Matzkevitsh and Vitke Kempner launched the first attack of the Partisans of the Vilna ghetto against the German Army, blowing up an ammunition column on the outskirts of the city. Hirsh Glik commemorated their deed in this Partisan song, one of the most beautiful of the Second World War.

Hal - tn a shpay-er in di hent? Tsi ge - hent?

1 Shtil, di nacht iz oysgeshternt,
Un der frost hot shtark gebrent.
Tsi gedenkstu vi ich hob dich gelernt
Haltn a shpayer in di hent?

2 A moyd, a peltsl un a beret,
Un halt in hant fest a nagan.
A moyd mit a sametenem ponim,
Hit op dem soyne's karavan.

3 Getsilt, geshosn un getrofn!
Hot ir kleyninker pistoyl.
An oto, a fulinkn mit vofn
Farhaltn hot zi mit eyn koyl!

4 Fartog, fun vald aroysgekrochn,
Mit shney girlandn oyf di hor.
Gemutikt fun kleyninkn nitsochn
Far undzer nayem, frayen dor!

1 Silence, and a starry night
Frost crackling, fine as sand.
Remember how I taught you
To hold a gun in your hand?

2 In fur jacket and beret,
Clutching a hand grenade,
A girl whose skin is velvet
Ambushes a cavalcade.

3 Aim, fire, shoot—and hit!
She, with her pistol small,
Halts an autoful,
Arms and all!

4 Morning, emerging from the wood,
In her hair, a snow carnation.
Proud of her small victory
For the new, free generation!

181

Zog Nit Keynmol

Hirsh Glik, poet and Partisan, was born in Vilna in 1920. During the German occupation, while confined to the concentration camp *Vayse Vake*, he wrote several poems which won him a prize from the Vilna ghetto. In 1943 all the Jews in *Vayse Vake* were brought to the Vilna ghetto and Glik joined the Partisans. At that time, inspired by the Warsaw ghetto uprising, he wrote this song; it was immediately chosen as the official hymn of the Jewish underground Partisan brigades. When the ghetto was liquidated, Glik was caught by the Gestapo and sent to a concentration camp in Estonia. During the Red Army's offensive in the Baltic area Glik escaped from the camp to nearby woods, where he died fighting the Germans.

Text: Hirsh Glik

Adapted from a melody by Pokras

Ku - men vet noch und - zer oys - ge - benk - te sho, S'vet a

poyk ton und - zer trot: mir ze - nen do! do!

Verses 2 and 4

Fun gri - nem pal - men land biz vay - tn land fun

shney Mir ku - men on mit undz - er payn, mit undz - er -

vey. Un vu ge - fal - n iz a shprits fun undz - er

blut, Shpro - tsn vet dort undz - er gvu - re, undz - er

mut. Vu ge - fal - n iz a shprits fon undz - er

D. C. al Fine

blut shpro - tsn vet dort undz - er gvu - re, undz - er mut!

D. C. al Fine

184

1   Zog nit keynmol az du geyst dem letstn veg,
Chotsh himlen blayene farshteln bloye teg;
Kumen vet noch undzer oysgebenkte sho,
S'vet a poyk ton undzer trot: mir zenen do!

2   Fun grinem palmen-land biz vaytn land fun
      shney,
Mir kumen on mit undzer payn, mit undzer vey;
Un vu gefaln iz a shprits fun undzer blut,
Shprotsn vet dort undzer g'vure, undzer mut.

3   S'vet di morgn-zun bagildn undz dem haynt,
Undzer nechtn vet farshvindn mitn faynt;
Nor oyb farzamen vet di zun un der kayor,
Vi a parol zol geyn dos lid fun dor tsu dor!

4   Dos lid geshribn iz mit blut un nit mit blay,
S'iz nit kayn lidl fun a foygl oyf der fray;
Dos hot a folk ts'vishn falndike vent
Dos lid gezungen mit naganes in di hent!

5   *Same as first verse*

1   Oh, never say that you have reached the very end,
Though leaden skies a bitter future may portend.
Because the hour for which we yearned will yet arrive
And our marching steps will thunder: We survive!

2   From land of palm trees to the land of distant snow,
We are here, with our pain, with our woe,
And wherever our blood was shed in pain,
Our fighting spirits will resurrect again.

3   Tomorrow's sun will gladden our today,
The past with bitter foe shall pass away.
But should the sun at dawn delay his coming,
Then let this clarion song ring out the future dawning.

4   Not lead, but blood, inscribed this song we sing,
It's not a caroling of birds upon the wing.
But 'twas a people midst the crashing fires of hell,
That sang this song, and fought courageous till it fell!

SONGS OF ISRAEL

In Israel new songs were born in the Hebrew language, expressing the dreams and aspirations of the young Jewish pioneers and reflecting the various occupations of their new life. The people sing of the joy of labor on the land, of the new road they are building through the desert wastes. They sing about the swamps they drain, the sheep they herd, the wheat they plant, the vineyards they tend. Many a song, too, has the warlike ring of a whole people engaged to the very death in defense of an age-old dream and, a homeland realized at last.

Although Israel has not had time enough to develop a distinctive musical character of its own, it has already produced a considerable number of songs, many in folk style, distinguished for color, spirit, beauty and verve. Community song and dance are an integral part of the life in Israel today

Zamri–Li

Yemenite Tune

Zam-ri-li, za-m-ri, Zam-ri-li, za-m-ri,

Yo - na____ t'-mi - ma. Za-m-ri-li gil mi

Tey - man.____ Ya-a-lu_lu, ya-a-lu, Tsi - yon____ miz-

ra - cha. Ya-a-lu Tsi - yon miz-ra - cha.____

188

Sing unto me, O sing,
Innocent dove.
Sing to me of the joy of Yemen.

Ascend, ascend
Into Zion, in the East.
Ascend to Zion in the East.

Sing unto me, O sing.

Kirya Y'feyfiya

Yemenite Melody

Kir - ya y' - fey - fi - ya, ma - sos le - a - ray - ich Ir ne - e - ma - na at le - mal - kech Ir ne - e - ma - na v' sa - ra - yich.

189

1 Kirya y'feyfiya, masos le-arayich
Ir ne-emana at lemalkech v'sarayich.

2 Yom ezk-ra yifat tsva-ayich,
Lach kalta nafshi lishkon chatserayich.

3 Umi yitneni a-uf kayonim,
Eshak avanayich achonen afarayich!

4 Lo shakta nafshi miyom n'dod ra-aya
Miyom g'lot banim mibet m'gurayich.

1 Lovely walled city, delight of cities,
City of fealty to kings and men.

2 Remembering the glory of your splendor,
My heart goes out with longing in your courts to dwell.

3 Oh that I might fly like the doves,
To kiss your stones and lie down in your dust!

4 No ease for my soul since that day
You wandered forth, your children exiled from home.

Shu–alim M'yal'lim

Shu - a - lim m' - ya - l' - lim.____ K'var cha - tsot.

V' - rak ha - ho - lech ba - tel ba - ley - lot, Ya -

vin et rim- zey ha- ko- cha- vim. Hit- as- fu shom- rim sa-

viv lam'- du- ra, V' sham na- gi- la, v'- nis- m'- cha!

Shu-alim m'yal'lim.
K'var chatsot.

V'rak haholech batel baleylot,
Yavin et rimzey hakochavim.

Hitasfu shomrim saviv lam'dura,
V'sham nagila, v'nism'cha!

Shu-alim m'yal'lim.
K'var chatsot.

The jackals howl.
It is midnight.

Only he who wanders idly in the night,
Understands the beckoning of the stars.

Gather, O watchmen, around the fire,
And there, let us sing and be merry!

The jackals howl.
It is midnight.

Kru–im Anu

ri - a mi - ni ch'ev. V' - ha - lev ya - ron ya - ri - a mi - ni ch'ev.

1 Kru-im anu, blu-yim anu,
Lichvod yomtov na-ade tlay al gabey tlay!
Hal'luya, Hal'luya,
Hal'luya ad b'li day!

Chorus:

V'halev paru-a v'ra-eyv,
V'halev yaron yari-a mini ch'ev.

2 R'eyvim anu, ts'meyim anu,
Lichvod yomtov nochal prusat lechem tsar!
Hal'luya, Hal'luya,
Hal'luya min hameytsar!

Chorus

3 *Same as first verse, but omit chorus*

1 Our clothes are worn, tattered and torn,
For the holiday we've patched our rags to wear,
Halleluja, Halleluja,
Halleluja fills the air.

Though the heart be hungry and rent with pain,
We shall sing and shout, again and yet again!

2 We are famished, we are thirsty,
For the holiday we've but dry crusts to share.
Halleluja, Halleluja,
Halleluja—out of our despair!

Shir Eres

Text: I. Halpern

Tune: Joel Engel

Chorus:

Numi, numi yaldati,
Numi, numi, nim.
Numi, numi k'tanati,
Numi, numi, nim . . .

Sleep, sleep, my baby girl,
Sleep, sleepy, sleep.
Sleep, sleep, my little girl,
Sleep, sleepy, sleep.

1   Aba halach la-avoda,
Halach, halach aba.
Yashuv im tset hal'vana,
Yavi lach matana.

Chorus

1   Daddy has gone off to work,
He's gone, he's gone away.
He'll be back when the moon comes out,
With a present for baby.

2   Aba halach el hakerem,
Halach, halach aba.
Yashuv im tset hakochavim,
Yavi lach anavim . . .

Chorus

2   Daddy has gone off to the field,
He's gone, he's gone away.
He'll be back when the stars come out,
With some grapes for baby.

Ali V'er

Text: Ch. N. Bialik

Tune: Sara Levy

195

Ali v'er
B'er ali
Uts'ki mey faz
M'lo hadli.

Se tsach varach,
Se tsame li,
Yavo v'yesht
Mimey hadli.

Rise, oh well,
Oh well, rise up,
Pour water clear
Into my bowl.

Tender young lamb,
My thirsty lamb,
Come drink the water,
From my bowl.

Shir Hakvish

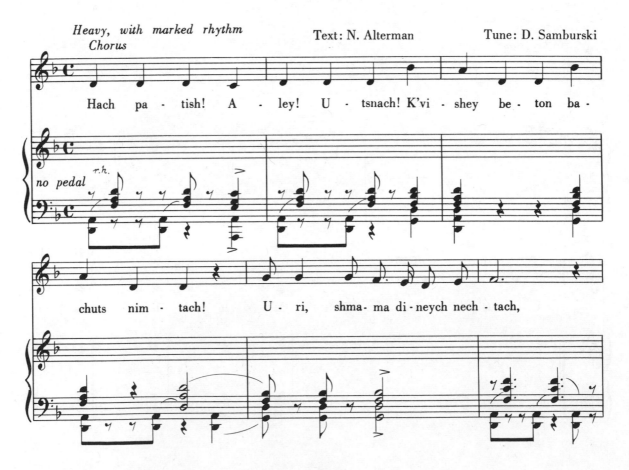

Heavy, with marked rhythm
Chorus

Text: N. Alterman

Tune: D. Samburski

Hach pa-tish! A-ley! U-tsnach! K'vi-shey be-ton ba-

chuts nim-tach! U-ri, shma-ma di-neych nech-tach,

196

Chorus:

Hach patish! Aley! Utsnach!
K'vishey beton bachuts nimtach!
Uri, shmama dineych nechtach,
Anu ba-im lichbosh otach.

Strike, strike with hammer in your hand,
As we lay concrete roads on sand.
Arise and bloom, O desert land,
For we have come to take command.

1 Dud bo-er ba-esh
Hamachbesh kovesh!
Hal-a! Hal-a, resh!
Ko-ach yesh vayesh!

    Chorus

1 Pitch boils on the fire.
New roads we desire.
Onward we aspire!
Strong men never tire!

2 Dud hazefet cham!
Yad notefet dam.
Kacha ben adam
Bamidbar nilcham!

    Chorus

2 The pitch blazes and
Blood drips from our hand.
Thus an earnest band
Wars with desert land!

197

Shir Ha-Emek

Emek Yizr'el, the valley of Jezreel, which lies between the hills of Shomron and Galilee, has during the past 25 years been transformed from a desert into a garden. Its 34 settlements include Tel Yosef, Eyn Charod, Nahalal, K'far Hasidim, and the town of Afula. The inhabitants of the Emek are deeply attached to their valley and have written many songs that describe its beauty with great tenderness.

Text: N. Alterman   Tune: D. Samburski

Ba - a m'nu - cha la - ya - ge - a, U - mar - go - a l' - a - mel.
Lay - la chi - ver mis - ta - re - a Al s'dot E - mek Yiz - r' - el.

Tal mil - ma - ta, u - lva - na me - al, Mi Bet Al - fa ad Na - ha - lal.

Ma, ma lay - la mi - leyl, D'ma - ma b' Yiz - r' - el.

Nu - ma E - mek, e - rets ti - fe - ret, A - nu l'-cha mish - me - ret!

1 Ba-a m'nucha layage-a,
Umargo-a l'amel.
Layla chiver mistare-a
Al s'dot Emek Yizr'el.
Tal milmata, ulvana me-al,
MiBet Alfa ad Nahalal.

Chorus:

Ma, ma layla mileyl,
D'mama b'Yizr-el,
Numa Emek, erets tiferet,
Anu l'cha mishmeret!

2 Yam hadagan mitno-e-a,
Shir ha-eder m'tsaltsel,
Zohi artsi usdoteha,
Zehu Emek Yizr'el.
Tvorach artsi v'tit-halal,
MiBet Alfa ad Nahalal.

Chorus

1 Now rest has come unto the weary,
And repose to him who toils.
Now the night lies pale upon
The rich fields of Esdraelon.
Dew below, moonlight over all,
From Bet Alfa to Nahalal.

Ah, ah, the day has gone.
Silence in Esdraelon.
Sleep, O valley, glorious land,
We are the watchmen at your hand.

2 The sea of ripening corn is swaying,
The sheepbells tinkle from afar,
This is my land I stand upon,
This is the valley Esdraelon.
Bless you, land, and fare you well,
From Bet Alfa to Nahalal.

Ruchot Hayam

Songs of the sea are something new in modern Jewish song. However, in Israel, which is bounded on the west by the Mediterranean, and embraces, besides, the Dead Sea, the Sea of Galilee (Sea of Kinneret), and the River Jordan, such songs must be regarded as a natural phenomenon: for Israel has already within the short span of a quarter century produced seamen and fishermen.

1 Ruchot hayam m'zamz'mim,
V'hagalim sharim, homim.
Hayam zorek po yahalomim
El hashamayim, hashamayim.
Bamerchakim to-a s'fina
Mifras lavan ka-anana,
Hayom yafa kol mangina,
Shiv'atayim, shiv'atayim!

2 Neytsey, nirkod na bama-agal
Nashir kol shir, nirdof kol gal.
Et hakadur nizrok el al!
El hashamayim, hashamayim.
Haru-ach kal, haru-ach cham,
Um'tsaltsel hats-chok haram.
Yafe hats-chok al s'fat hayam
Shiv'atayim, shiv'atayim!

1 The winds chant across the sea,
The waves they murmur gently,
Bright gems are cast up to the sky,
Into the air, into the air.
A vessel passes far away,
Its sails are waving, white and gay,
The singing is so sweet today,
Beyond compare, beyond compare.

2 We'll all go dancing in a ring,
We'll race the waves and racing, sing!
And then a ball we'll catch and fling!
Into the air, into the air!
The wind is gentle, the breeze so warm,
Loud laughter rings out all around.
Filling the air with joyous sound!
Beyond compare, beyond compare!

Artsa Alinu

The Hora, national dance of Israel, was originally a Rumanian folk dance. In Palestine, however, it underwent many changes and now it shows characteristics distinctive of the Yishuv. The Hora here is one of many that modern Israel dances to.

Ar - tsa a - li - nu. Ar - tsa a - li - nu. Ar - tsa a - li - nu.

K'var cha - rash - nu v' - gam za - ra - nu.

A - val od lo ka - tsar - nu. A - val od lo ka -

Artsa alinu.
K'var charashnu v'gam zara-anu,
Aval od lo katsarnu.

We have come to the land, our home.
We have plowed and we have sown,
But we've not yet reaped our own.

Zirmu Galim

Zir - mu ga - lim, __ pe - leg __ z'rom, De - rech har __ va - gay,

La - a - hu - va - ti __ sa sha - lom B'ra - cha ad __ b'li __ day.

2 Saper, saper, peleg la
Ota ma ohav!
Kama k'shura nafshi va
Tsa-ari ma hu rav.

3 Saper, peleg na-im la,
Et ga-agu-ay dom,
Biladeha chayay ma?
Saviv reyk, shomem.

1 Flow, O waves, O stream flow on,
Over hill and dell.
Flow to where my loved one's gone,
Greet her, wish her well.

2 Tell her of my love profound,
Tell her, as you flow,
How my soul to her is bound,
Tell of my great woe.

3 Here I pine in secrecy—
Tell her, friendly stream,
That without her, life to me
Is an empty dream.

Se Ug'di

Text and Tune: M. Weiner

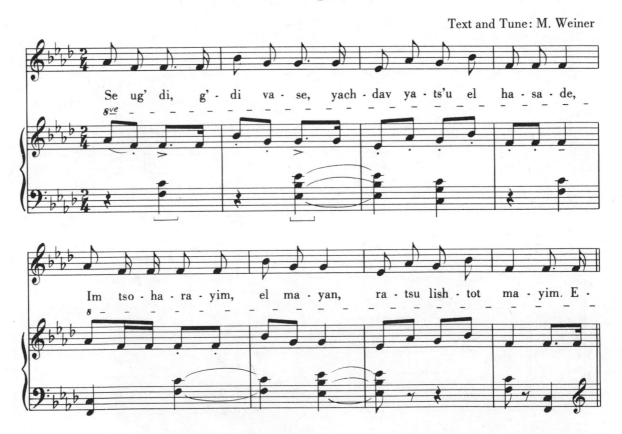

Se ug' di, g'-di va-se, yach-dav ya-ts'u el ha-sa-de,

Im tso-ha-ra-yim, el ma-yan, ra-tsu lish-tot ma-yim. E-

chad la-van, she-ni sh'char-char, im tal-ta-ley oz-na-yim,
Pa-a-mo-nim m'-tsal'-ts'-lim _ al tsa-va-rey a_-_da-yim.__

El _ ha-ma-yan, ra-tsu a-da-rim. ra-tsu a-da-rim.

1 Se ug'di, g'di vase, yachdav yats'u el hasade,
Im tsoharayim, el mayan, ratsu lishtot mayim.
Echad lavan, sheni sh'-charchar, im taltaley
    oznayim,
Pa-amonim m'tsal'ts'lim al tsavarey adayim.
El hamayan, ratsu adarim.

2 Yashvu la-arets haro-im, rega kat lanu-ach,
Pat bashemen to-amim, v'zahav tapu-ach.
Utsu, rutsu, shovavim, hasimcha ko terev—
Habayta od m'at shavim, hiney ba ha-erev.
Li, li, li, li, ranen chalili.

1 A lamb and a kid, a kid and a lamb went into the field
    together,
Ran at noontime to the wellspring, ran to drink the water.
The first was white, the second black, and both had curly
    ear-locks,
Bells ringing on their throats.
To the wellspring ran the flocks.

2 The shepherds sat down on the earth for a moment's
    halt,
To eat a golden orange and a slice of bread with salt.
Go on, run, you rascals, you're having such grand fun,
We'll be going home soon, the day is about done.
Li, li, li, li, play on my flute.

205

Mi Yivne Hagalil?

2   Poalim yivnu haGalil!
Poalot tivnena haGalil!
Mi yivne haGalil?
El yivne haGalil.

     Chorus

3   G'dolim yivnu haGalil!
G'dolot tivnena haGalil!
Mi yivne haGalil?
El yivne haGalil.

Who will build Galilee?
The Lord will build Galilee.

1 The sons will build Galilee.
The daughters will build Galilee.

2 The workmen will build Galilee.
The workwomen will build Galilee.

3 Great men will build Galilee.
Great women will build Galilee.

Y'mey Hanoar

1 Y'mey hanoar
Chalfu avaru.
Imi, arsi li,
Hoy, ima,
Na-ara y'feyfiya.

2 B'tsel hazayit,
Makom nistar m'ayin.
Sham techake-li,
Hoy, ima,
Yafati han'ima.

1 The days of my bloom
Have gone and passed.
Mother, betroth me soon!
Oh, mother!
That girl is lovely.

2 In the shade of the olive tree,
There is a secret place.
She's waiting there for me.
Oh, mother!
My darling is lovely!

Gilu Hagalilim (Hora)

This song relates to the early twenties of the 20th century, and to the struggle for Galilee. Mounted and armed, the watchmen of that period (*shomrim, notrim*), played an important part, guarding the vineyards, protecting the young Jewish settlements. Many lost their lives then and those who survived formed the core of the later-organized Haganah.

Gi - lu   ha - Ga - lil - im, gi - bo - rey ha - cha - yil   Si - su v' - sim - chu___

yo - mam va - la - yil.   Gi - lu   ha - Ga - lil - im, gi - bo - rey ha - cha - yil

Si - su v' - sim - chu   yo - mam va - lay - il.   Gi - lu   ha - Ga - lil - im, gi -

bo·rey ha·cha·yil Si su v'·sim·chu____yo·mam va·la·yil.

D. C. al Fine

1 Gilu haGalilim, giboreye hachayil
Sisu v'simchu yomam valayil.

2 Meycheshkat halayil ole kol chalil,
Shiro yashmia shomer haGalil.

3 Yeheme haGalil, ko yeheme l'vavi
Susi kal-raglayim, daruch hu rovi.

4 Zulat-cha haGalil, ma li vami li?
HaGalil, Galili, ach ata Galili.

1 Sing Galileans, ye heroes of battle,
Rejoice and be merry all day and all night.

2 Through the dark nights, the sweet-sounding flute,
Song of the watchmen of Galilee.

3 Aroused is Galilee, so heaves my heart,
Fleet is my steed and my rifle poised.

4 I have only you, my own Galilee,
Galilee, you are my all.

209

B'tel Chay

Joseph Trumpeldor was born in Pyatigorsk in the Caucasus in 1880. He fought in the Russo-Japanese war, was wounded, and lost his arm. He was decorated, presented with an artificial arm, and raised to the rank of officer in the reserve corps—the first Jewish officer in the czarist army. In 1912 he migrated to Palestine and established a commune at Migdal. In 1915, serving under British command, he distinguished himself at Gallipoli. When the French forces withdrew from upper Galilee in 1920, the Jewish colonies of Metulla, K'far Giladi, Tel Chay and Chamara were in danger of being attacked by Arab bands. Trumpeldor organized a defense corps of about fifty, including some men of the American Jewish Legion. This band held out for two months, but on March 1, 1920, Trumpeldor fell at Tel Chay with five of his men. His last words were: *Eyn davar, tov lamut b'ad artseynu* (It is all right; it is good to die for our country).

1   Ba-Galil, b'Tel Chay, Trumpeldor nafal.
B'ad ameynu, b'ad artseynu, gibor Yoseef nafal.
Derech harim derech g'va-ot, rats lig'ol et shem
  Tel-Chay,
Leymor l'achim sham: "l'chu b'ikvotay!"

2   "B'chol makom, uv'chol rega, tizk'ru oti,
Ki nilchamti, v'gam nafalti, b'ad molad'ti!
Kol hayom ani charashti, uvalayla,
K'ney rovi b'yadi achazti ad harega ha-achron."

1   In Galilee, in Tel-Chay, Trumpeldor the hero, fell.
For our people, for our land, the hero Joseph, fell.
Over hill and over dale to redeem Tel-Chay, sped he.
Crying to his brothers: "Follow, after me!"

2   "Every place and every hour, remember me, remember
  me.
For I battled and I fell for my Galilee.
I plowed the land. I watched my land.
And fell with the rifle in my hand."

Beyn N'har Prat Un'har Chidekel

Text: Ch. N. Bialik

1   Beyn n'har Prat un'har Chidekel,
Al hahar mitamer dekel,
Uvadekel beyn afa-av
Tishkon la duchifat zahav.

2   Tsipor zahav, ufi, chugi,
Ts'i uvakshi li ben zugi,
Uvaasher timtsa-ihu,
Kifti oto vahavi-ihu.

3   Ach im eyn lach chut hashani,
Dabri shalom el chatani,
Uma tagidi lo? hagidi:
Nafshi yots'et el yedidi.

4   Imri lo, hagan poreyach,
Na-ul hu, v'eyn poteyach,
Rimon paz sham yesh beyn alav
Ach eyn mi shey'varech alav.

1 Between the Tigris and Euphrates,
A date palm rises on the hill.
On a branch of the palm
Rests a golden whippoorwill.

2 Fly off, O golden bird, fly off,
Fly off, and find my husband-to-be,
And when at last you come upon him,
Bind and bring him back to me.

3 But if you have no crimson thread,
Speak soothingly to him instead.
What will you say to him? Why say,
My heart longs for him all day.

4 Say too, the garden is in flower,
And none 'to open the locked bower.
A golden date hangs on the tree,
But there is none to stop and see.

Molad'ti

My place of birth is the land of Canaan.
I would go forth to the fields of Choran.

NOTE. Sung twice through; the second time to the syllables: "Yalel, Yalel, Yalel," etc.

Shir Ha-Palmach

The Jewish Brigade (some 5,000 strong), which fought on the side of the Allies in Africa and Italy, sang many a song, and here is one that it created. This particular song became one of the most popular with the Haganah, of which Palmach was the military striking arm.

Beyn g'vu- lot bi-dra-chim l'- lo de- - rech, B' leylot cha-shu-chey ko-cha-vim, Sha-ya-ra shel a-chim l'- lo
he- -ref, La-mo-le-det a-nu m'-la-vim.

1   Beyn g'vulot bidrachim l'lo derech,
B'leylot chashuchey kochavim,
Shayara shel achim l'lo heref,
Lamoledet anu m'lavim.

Chorus:

   La-olel, v'larach,
   She-arim po niftach!
   Lamach v'lazaken
   Anu po chomat magen!

2   Im hasha-ar sagur, eyn pote-ach,
Et hasha-ar nishbor v'nitots,
Kol choma b'tsura n'nage-ach
V'chol sedek narchiv v'nifrots.

  Chorus

3   Shayara, al b'chi v'al tsa-ar,
Hisha-en al z'ro-i sav zaken,
Gam laze shesagar et hasha-ar
Yom yavo shel nakam v'shillem.

  Chorus

1 Between the borders, on pathless byways,
On pitch-dark nights, when no stars appear,
A company of brothers go marching, marching,
For the homeland we are marching here.

For the helpless and the young,
Wide the gates we fling!
For the aged and the lame,
The shield of victory we bring!

2 And should the gates be locked and barred,
We'll break and batter them down.
Every encirclement we will pierce!
Every rampart will be ours!

3 Oh, brothers, no tears and no mourning,
Lean on our strength, ye aged and weak,
Even for those still at the barred gates
A day of bitter reckoning waits!

Zemer Lach (Hora)

Ze - mer, ze - mer lach! Ze - mer, ze - mer lach!
Ha - ma - chol so - vev, ze - mer lach do - vev,

Ze - mer lach m' - cho - ra - ti, m' - cho - ra - ti.
Ze - mer lach m' - cho - ra - ti, m' - cho - ra - ti!

Ha - r' - ra - yich he - ma yis - ma - chu, Eyt m' - chol - ha - ho - ra yis' -

no pedal

216

1 Zemer, zemer lach! Zemer, zemer lach!
Zemer lach m'chorati, m'chorati.
Hamachol sovev, zemer lach dovev,
Zemer lach m'chorati, m'chorati!

Chorus:

Har-rayich hema yismachu,
Eyt m'chol-hahora yis'ar,
Elef prachim l'feta yifrachu
Y'chasu et p'ney hamidbar!

1 We sing a song to you, a song to you,
To you our land of birth, my native land.
The ring goes round, our song resounds,
To you, our land of birth, my native land.

The hills and mountains too, rejoice,
The Hora whirls around—
A thousand blossoms bursting forth
Will soon bedeck this desert ground!

2 Telem, telem, lach! Telem, telem lach!
Telem lach m'chorati, m'chorati!
Hamachol sovev, zemer lach dovev,
Telem lach m'chorati, m'chorati!

Chorus

3 Hora, hora hach! Hora, hora hach!
Hora lach, m'chorati, m'chorati!
Hamachol sovev, zemer lach dovev,
Hora lach m'chorati, m'chorati!

Chorus

2 We plow for you, we plow for you,
For you, our land of birth, my native land!

3 We dance to you, we dance to you,
To you, our land of birth, my native land!

Shir La–Negev

The Negev (South) has from ancient times figured in Jewish history. It was
here that the Patriarchs dug their first wells and watered their sheep. In
recent years, with the establishment of a number of Jewish settlements (the
largest being Bet Eshel, Revivim, Gevulot), certain areas of the sandy wastes
have been put under cultivation.

D. C. al Fine

mi yar - vey - nu? Mi yit - ney - nu ma - yim?

D. C. al Fine

2 Ki tsameyta gam kivita
Regev rigvotayim.
Od narvecha, v'ravita
Od narvecha mayim!

Chorus

3 Od narvecha, od nivnecha,
Negev, v'nivneyta!
T'mol nichsafnu od: ayeka?
V'hayom—nigleyta!

Chorus

1 Have you heard how in the Negev
Land against the sky,
Every clod of parched earth prays for
Water lest it die?

Water, water, give us water!
We're athirst for water.
We're athirst, who'll be the first
To quench our thirst with water?

2 Parched, you waited for your hour,
Now it is at hand.
We'll bring water and you'll flower—
Water for the land.

3 We shall water you and build you,
You shall be recovered.
Yesterday, who knew, who tilled you?
Now—you are discovered!

Yafim Haleylot BiChna–an

Ya - fim ha - ley - lot bi - Chna - an, Tso - n' - nim hem, u - v' - hi -

rim.   V' - ha - d' - ma - ma pal - ta shir,___ Ya - an li - bi b' - shir.___

Yi - l' - lat ta - nim nu - ga, ___ Tech' - tse d'mi ha - la - yil.

2   Achay halchu lir'ot tsonam,
L'hashkot ha-adarim.
V'Rachel, Rachel sheli,
M'kapetset al harim.

   Chorus

3   Hasheleg al haChermon
Holech v'nameys,—
Bo-i elay, Rachel sheli,
Bo-i na, v'nitaleys!

   Chorus

1   Lovely are the nights in Canaan,
Lovely, and clear, and cool.
The silence sings around me,
My heart wells up in song.

The wail of the jackals is sweetly sad,
Cleaving the stillness of the night.

2   My brethren have gone to pasture the flock,
They will water the sheep.
And Rachel, Rachel, my beloved,
Bounds over the hillocks and hills.

3   The snow on top of Mount Hermon,
Is slowly melting away—
Come to me, Rachel, my beloved,
Come, let us leap and play!

Birkat Am (Tech'zakna)

Text: Ch. N. Bialik

March-like

Tech' - zak - na y' - dey kol a - chey - nu ham - cho - n' - nim

Af - rot ar - tsey - nu ba - a - sher hem sham; Al

yi - pol ru - cha - chem a - li - zim, mit - ro - n' - nim

Bo - u sh'chem e - chad l' ez - rat ha - am! Al l' ez - rat ha - am!

Strengthen the hands of our brothers, caressing
The soil of our land, wherever they be.

Keep high your spirits, with joy abounding
Go shoulder to shoulder to set your folk free!

Hatikvah

Text: N. H. Imber

Kol___ od ba-ley-vav p'-ni-ma, Ne-fesh Y'-hu-di
ho-mi-ya, Ul'-fa-a tey___ miz-rach ka-di-ma,
A-yin l'-Tsi-yon tso-fi-ya. Od lo av-da
tik-va-tey-nu, Ha-tik-vah shnot al-pa-yim,

Li - h'yot am chof - shi b' - ar - tsey - nu E - rets Tsi - yon vi - Ru - sha - la - yim. Li - h'yot am chof - shi b' - ar - tsey - nu E - rets Tsi - yon vi - Ru - sha - la - yim.

Kol od baleyvav p'nima,
Nefesh Y'hudi homiya,
Ul-fa-ate mizrach kadima,
Ayin l'Tsiyon tsofiya.

As long as in a Jewish breast,
The soul's stirring has not ceased,
The eye for longing will not rest
Until it gaze on Zion in the East.

Chorus:

Od lo avda tikvateynu,
  Hatikvah shnot alpayim,
  Lih-yot am chofshi b'artseynu
Erets Tsiyon vi-Rushalayim.

Our ancient hope will not perish
Hope from ages long since past.
To live free in the land we cherish,
Zion and Jerusalem, at last.

223

Selected Bibliography

[Names of persons indicate editors and compilers of the volumes, except where an appended (A) indicates "author."]

Beregovski, M. *Jidiser Muzik-folklor* (Moscow 1934)

Bronzaft, M., *and* Samburski, D. *Sefer Shirim Umanignot* (Jerusalem 1946)

Brounoff, P. *Jewish Folksongs* (New York 1911)

Cahan, J. L. *Yiddish Folksongs* (New York 1912)

Cahan, J. L. *Yidisher Folklor* (Vilna 1938)

Engel, J. *50 Yidishe Kinderlider* (Berlin 1923)

Fefer, I., *and* Beregovski, M. *Yidishe Folkslider* (Kiev 1938)

Gebirtig, M. (A) *Mayne Lider* (Cracow 1936)

Ginsburg, S., *and* Marek, P. *Yevreiskiya Narodniya Pesni* (St. Petersburg 1901)

Hirschler, Z. *Shirey Am* (Zagreb s.a.)

Idelsohn, A. Z. *Tsliley ha-Arets* (Berlin 1922)

Idelsohn, A. Z. *Sefer Hashirim* (Berlin and Jerusalem 1912)

Kaufman, F. M. *Die Schoensten Lieder Der Ostjuden* (Berlin 1920)

Kipnis, M. *60 Folkslider* (Warsaw 1918-1925)

Kipnis, M. *80 Folkslider* (Warsaw 1918-1925)

Kisselgof, Z. *Lieder Zamlbuch* (Berlin 1911)

Kacerginski, S. *Dos Gezang Fun Vilner Geto* (Paris 1947)

Kotylansky, C. *Folks-gezangen* (Los Angeles 1944)

Prilutsky, N. *Yidishe Folkslider* (Warsaw 1910)

Sapira, Y. *Shir Umizmor L'Chayil* (Tel Aviv 1945)

Sapira, Y. *Shirey Avoda Umoledet* (Tel Aviv 1945)

Sheinberg, J. *Shirey Erets Israel* (Berlin 1935)

Warshavsky, M. M. *A Yidishe Folkslider* (New York 1918)

Translators

RUTH RUBIN translated the songs on pages: 94, 140, 158, 182, 190, 202, 208, 213, 216 and 219.

ISAAC SCHWARTZ translated the songs on pages: 100, 114, 144, 152, 164, 192, 196 and 203.

JACOB SLOAN translated the songs on pages: 17, 20, 22, 23, 25, 35, 36, 38, 42, 44, 49, 53, 60, 61, 66, 70, 72, 79, 80, 86, 108, 114, 120, 124, 130, 132, 142, 146, 148, 162, 170, 176, 180, 198, 204, 210 and 212.

Translations of the remaining songs were revised by the editor.

The translations are in many instances free renditions from the Yiddish or the Hebrew. They are intended to give an idea of the content of the songs and are not meant to be sung.